Royal
Botanic Garden
Edinburgh

Plants:
Healers and
Killers

Michael Radcliffe Lee

ISBN: 978-1-906129-96-5

Published by
Royal Botanic Garden Edinburgh
20A Inverleith Row, Edinburgh, EH3 5LR
www.rbge.org.uk

Printed by Meigle Colour Printers Limited
using vegetable-based inks and eco-friendly varnish,
under the control of an Environmental Management System.

Contents

Foreword

The 17th-century physician Robert Sibbald, a major figure of the Enlightenment and an arch-protagonist of the College of Physicians in Edinburgh, appreciated the importance of botany and other branches of science to therapeutics, writing, "I resolved to make it part of my studie to know what animalls, mineralls, metalls and substances cast up by the sea, were found in this country, that might be of use in medicine, or other artes usefull to human lyfe …". It was he, along with his friend and colleague Andrew Balfour, who established the Physick Garden in the grounds of Holyrood Abbey in 1667, the forerunner of the present Royal Botanic Garden in Inverleith.

In my career in medicine, spanning some 50 years, I have witnessed a seemingly never-ending procession of complex and hugely effective synthetic drugs. However, there is now real anxiety that the pipeline may be drying up, and so the pharmaceutical industry is beginning to fund research into the potential benefits of plant extracts, many of which have been used for centuries in the develeoping world. The colonisation of Africa, beyond its Mediterranean shores, would not have been possible but for the efficacy of quinine, an extract of Peruvian bark, in the treatment and prevention of malaria.

John Kirk, who trained in the Royal Infirmary of Edinburgh, was medical officer, botanist and photographer on David Livingstone's second Zambezi expedition between 1858 and 1863. His decision to issue quinine daily as a prophylactic undoubtedly reduced the anticipated mortality rate significantly. He would observe at first hand cinchonism, the constellation of ringing in the ears, temporary deafness and even blindness resulting from excessive dosage. Dr Kirk, an undoubted polymath, became Consul General in Zanzibar where he succeeded, against all odds, in persuading the Sultan to cease the lucrative slave trade.

In this wonderful collection of beautifully illustrated essays which are more than a passing tribute to Sibbald, Professor Lee reveals an incredible depth of knowledge, reminds us of the importance of plants in medical history and almost certainly in the future, and informs us of their potential as poisons, properties of which the criminal, the warrior and the witch doctor have been very aware.

Anthony Toft, former physician, Royal Infirmary, Edinburgh

Foreword

How can it be that at least one in five plant species is threatened with extinction when plants are the basis for life on earth? How can it be that the planet's stock of natural capital which underpins our economy and wellbeing is undergoing rapid depletion and disastrous degradation? How can it be that some plants are becoming extinct even before they have been studied by scientists?

In this wonderfully illustrated and researched book Professor Michael Radcliffe Lee articulates in an entertaining style how plants and fungi provide therapeutic advantage, reinforcing the urgent necessity for more action to be taken to protect our natural capital and the critical need to sustain high-quality plant science.

Botany and medicine are intimately inter-linked. Early botanical science was dominated by research into the medicinal properties of plants, and we can thank the scientists of the 17th century for establishing physic gardens that were the precursors of many contemporary botanic gardens including the Royal Botanic Garden Edinburgh. It should therefore be no surprise that an eminent professor of medicine is writing about the history, mythology and medicinal properties of some of our best known, and in some cases notorious, plants.

Plants: Healers and Killers takes the reader on a journey across the world through the centuries, revealing the mysteries of 16 extraordinary plants including the discovery of the "essential medicine" atropine, the use of Calabar beans in trials by ordeal and how the infamous Dr Crippen murdered his wife in 1910. It also reveals how scientists continue to discover the power of plant-related alkaloids for modern medicines, such as the anti-cancer agent taxel, originally derived from yew, and galantamine, extracted from snowdrops and used to treat Alzheimer's disease.

Through linking ancient practices and traditions with contemporary science Professor Lee reveals the evolution of medicinal plant science and the extraordinary ability of plants to kill and heal. What cures in plants remain to be discovered and how many have we lost? I very much hope that this book will inspire more people to take action to reverse the rapid loss of plant diversity and to gain a deeper insight into the amazing relationship between plants and humans.

Simon Milne MBE FRGS
Regius Keeper
Royal Botanic Garden Edinburgh

Introduction

When I retired from active clinical practice some years ago I was temporarily at a loss as to which interests I should pursue in my new-found leisure time. After several false starts and no real progress, one Saturday I picked up the *Daily Telegraph* in a rather desultory way. The front page of the gardening supplement described a nationwide appeal for all gardeners to send cuttings of the yew (*Taxus baccata*) to central collecting points, rather than burning them. They were to be used by pharmaceutical companies to extract new compounds, later to be called docetaxel and paclitaxel. These agents would prove to be very powerful anti-cancer agents and are now widely used in treatments.

Knowing something of the history of the yew and its reputation as a deadly poison to cattle and horses, I decided to write an article on the plant in mythology and medicine, and this was subsequently published in *The Journal of the Royal College of Physicians of Edinburgh*. The article was greeted with some enthusiasm and the fire was duly lit. Since that time I have written a series of articles on plants and how they have been turned to therapeutic advantage. Several kind critics suggested that these articles should be gathered together in one volume and this I have now attempted to do in this book. A number of the articles have been rewritten in order to make them accessible to the non-chemist and the gardener. I also include some information on the autonomic nervous system, as many of the plants described have their effects on this system and in particular on the balance between adrenaline and acetylcholine in the human body.

This book is not exhaustive; there are, of course, notable absentees from the list of plants included. Many would expect to find Erythroxylaceae (for cocaine), *Papaver*

somniferum (for opium) and cannabis (for the cannabinoids). Any of these plants and their associated drugs could fill a volume by themselves and they have regularly done so. My list is unashamedly one which reflects my own developing interest.

Caught up in this book are murder, suicide, trial by ordeal, accidental poisoning and drugs which have changed the face of modern medicine. Any substance, when given in a great enough quantity, can be lethal, and the plants covered in this book differ in toxicity. Some, such as henbane and deadly nightshade, have been known poisons for as far back as records allow, whilst the dangers of others, such as St John's wort, were defined in the twentieth century. Some of the plants can both heal and kill whilst others tend towards only one of these characteristics and all, however overlooked previously, deserve our interest. My purpose has been to inform, to educate and to entertain and I hope my reader will agree it has been fulfilled.

The following information in this introduction explains some of the more complicated concepts described in the following chapters. Readers may prefer to come back to it once they have read the main text.

An Explanation of the Preparation of Active Compounds from Plants

Plant alkaloids can be defined as nitrogen-containing, organic compounds that form the basis of pharmacologically-active derivatives of plants – often, but not always, from flowering species. Somewhere in the region of 10,000 such compounds have been prepared from various plant species, over many centuries. Until quite recently the natural function of these compounds within plants remained relatively poorly understood. It was once thought that many were simply by-products of normal plant metabolism. It is now increasingly clear that these substances often play roles in defence and repair, such as UV-protection, within plants. The central interest in their pharmacological properties in humans, however, remains uppermost amongst many researchers in this field.

Extraction of plant alkaloids has historically relied upon collection of sufficient (usually large) quantities of the appropriate plant material, which is finely ground or homogenised. Most source plants tend to contain a mixture of different alkaloids and therefore individual extraction methods vary widely. Generally, though, either an acid or base extraction method is used to obtain the crude mix of substances. Once in solution, the desired components can be extracted using an appropriate inorganic solvent. This extraction can be repeated several times to increase purity. Individual alkaloids of interest can then be isolated based on known properties – for example by distillation, or by extraction with a specific solvent.

At an industrial level, many alkaloids are still isolated using variations of the basic methods outlined above. However, yield and cost have driven advances in the uses of synthetic chemical approaches. Many pharmacologically important alkaloids can now be chemically synthesised in the laboratory, improving both yield and efficiency. Moreover, understanding the genetic pathways used by plants to synthesise alkaloids has allowed further advances in their production. For example, there is now the potential to genetically modify plants to increase their content of the alkaloids of interest.

It is also noteworthy that modern approaches to chemical analysis and molecular fingerprinting have added impetus to the high-throughput screening of plant-derived compounds in an attempt to identify active components. Thus not only is modern technology aiding in the understanding and optimisation of compounds which may have been used for hundreds, or even thousands, of years, it is also contributing to the identification and development of new compounds with therapeutic potential.

A Word on the Nervous System

In order to understand the physiological information in this book a certain understanding of the way drugs work in the human body is useful. When we think about the nervous system generally we are conscious of thought, action and the stimuli of the senses, a system which determines our relationship with the world around us. But within the mammalian body there is another hidden nervous system which acts automatically 24 hours a day, sleeping or waking. This system controls, amongst other functions, heart rate, blood pressure, breathing and the actions of the stomach, small and large intestines. It is called the autonomic (meaning automatic) nervous system (ANS), and it functions largely beyond our control, although some elements of its activity can be consciously modified under particular circumstances (e.g. the lowering of blood pressure and heart rate through meditation).

The ANS is regulated by higher control centres within the brain, which integrate inputs received from sensory nerves, our emotions and the environment and generate an appropriate outward (efferent) response.

It is a rapidly responding system, matching many of the body's major physiological outputs to its current requirements at any given time. It should be stressed that whilst the features below are based around two extreme situations, the ANS output is constantly being fine-tuned in order to adjust to even very small changes in activity, such as posture, mood and temperature.

The ANS can be divided into two main branches;
• **the sympathetic nervous system**
• **the parasympathetic nervous system**

Classically, these two systems are often described as acting in opposition to each other, with the net output determining the physiological effects of current ANS activity on a second-to-second basis. This dichotomy is now recognised as an over-simplification, but for many physiological actions the basic principle holds true.

The sympathetic nervous system: "fight or flight" responses

Activation of the sympathetic nervous system can most easily be thought of within an evolutionary framework, with responsibility for coordinating the body's response to threat, danger or excitement. For example, for our ancestors fleeing from – or fighting to the death with – a predator species, increased activation of certain bodily functions was useful. The force and rate of contraction of the heart would increase, and the blood pressure would rise, preparing the body

for an increase in physical exertion. Pupils would dilate, allowing more light to enter the eye and thus improve vigilance. The person would experience a dry mouth and gut muscle activity would be inhibited as the body focused resources on being able to run or fight effectively. The airways would dilate, facilitating increased ventilation of the lungs and meeting an increased demand for oxygen. Signals would be sent to the body's energy stores in the liver to increase the supply of glucose to the muscles.

The parasympathetic nervous system: "rest and digest" responses

As previously mentioned, in general the main effects of the parasympathetic nervous system can be thought of as opposing those of the sympathetic system. For example, the force and rate of contraction of the heart both decrease, with the resulting reduction of cardiac output contributing to a lowering of blood pressure. The airways respond by constricting, glandular secretions increase and the activity of the gastrointestinal system becomes more pronounced. The body enters into a state of rest, with its resources directed more towards activities such as digestion, rather than running or fighting.

The activation of the ANS is transmitted throughout the body via a specialised network of neurones. Both branches of the system consist of two neurones in series, separated by a tiny, specialised gap (known as a synapse) at what is termed a ganglion. Signals are passed down the pre-ganglionic neurones via electrical activity. At the ganglion the signal is conveyed by chemicals referred to as neurotransmitters. For both branches of the ANS, the ganglionic neurotransmitter is acetylcholine. This substance diffuses across the synaptic gap, combining with particular receptor proteins on the other side, which in turn initiates a further chain of electrical activity. When the post-ganglionic neurone is stimulated in this manner it releases neurotransmitters which diffuse across a second synapse, this time interacting with receptor proteins on the cells of the target tissues. These receptors are in turn linked to various pathways that generate the final response.

There are a number of points in ANS neurotransmission where compounds – including plant-derived drugs – are able to influence activity. In the sympathetic nervous system, the main neurotransmitter released at the target tissue is usually noradrenaline. Drugs discussed in this book which mimic this effect (known as adrenergics or sympathomimetics) include ephedrine. Drugs that block the effect include ergotamine. In the parasympathetic system, the main postganglionic neurotransmitter is again acetylcholine, although here acting on a different type of receptor than at the ganglion. Drugs that mimic parasympathetic effects (known as cholinergics) include physostigmine, galantamine and hypericin. Drugs that block this function (known as

anticholinergics) include atropine, hyoscine, solanine and tubocurarine.

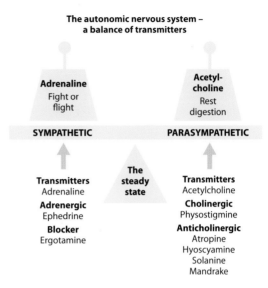

For those of you who have not opened a chemistry book since schooldays the chemical diagrams used in this book illustrate the molecular structures of the compounds. They show the arrangements of the atoms and how they are bonded and give some understanding of these chemicals and their complexity. All biological compounds can occur in right- and left-handed forms (d or dextro and l or laevo). These are the so-called isomers of the basic compound. The important point is that an l-form can be extremely poisonous while its d-form is inactive and may even oppose (or block) the action of the l-form on the body.

Atropa Belladonna L.

N. d. Natur v. W. Müller.

1 – Deadly Nightshade (*Atropa belladonna*): The Beautiful Lady

Deadly nightshade (*Atropa belladonna*) is a plant with a long history. The plant contains the toxic alkaloid atropine (dl-hyoscyamine); and while best known as a poison, when atropine is administered in small doses it has a variety of medicinal uses. As access to atropine grew more limited in the course of the 20th century, its use as a poison became less common. In 1994, however, a biochemistry lecturer from Edinburgh tried to poison his wife with the pure alkaloid. Fortunately, his attempt was not to prove fatal, but this was more down to good luck than to any other factor.

The genus *Atropa* comprises a group of three species of large perennial herbs. It belongs to the family Solanaceae, so is related to tobacco, the potato and the tomato. The plant's simple leaves and bell-shaped flowers with five-lobed purple-brown petals are quite distinctive. The genus is widely distributed from Western Europe to the Himalayas and grows in disturbed ground and woodland margins. The best known species is *A. belladonna* which has erect stems up to 2 m in height. The fruit is a black berry. All parts of the plant are poisonous, particularly the berries.

The History of Deadly Nightshade

The plant was well known to the Ancient Greeks, who realised that it was extremely poisonous and thus associated it with Atropos, one of the three Fates who were said to control the length of every mortal's life: Clotho would spin the thread; Lachesis would measure it off and Atropos would sever it when the time came for the person to die. Indeed, it is likely that *Atropa* was the potion that the sorceress Circe administered to the sailors on Odysseus' ship, as recounted in Homer's *Odyssey*. The drug, it is said, drove the sailors mad and turned them into swine. Odysseus, however, resisted the poison by taking the magical herb known as 'moly', given to him by Hermes, in order to protect him from its effects; it is thought that this may well be the snowdrop (*Galanthus nivalis*) (see Chapter 5).

The *Atropa* plant later became associated with the cult of Dionysus, the Greek god of fertility and wine. It is said that worshippers dissolved *Atropa*, ivy and other plants in wine to create a magic potion. On consuming this

The three goddesses of fate in Greek mythology. The eldest, Atropos, was said to control the length of life by cutting its thread, so the poisonous nature of the plant associated it with her actions.

potion, the devotees passed into a trance during which they danced with abandon and committed lewd and libidinous acts. Those initiated into the rite were promised eternal life and continued sexual potency.

The Greeks often confused *Atropa* with the mandrake (*Mandragora*) and, indeed, they are closely related members of the Solanaceae family. The first person to recognise that *Atropa* was in fact a distinct plant was the Greek physician and botanist Pedanius Dioscorides of Anazarba (c. AD 40–90), widely regarded as the father of pharmacology. Born in Cilicia, Dioscorides travelled extensively through the whole of southern Europe, investigating more than 600 different herbs and recording his findings. He realised that *Atropa* should not be used in preference to *Mandragora* as a medicinal herb because its effects were much more poisonous.

Pietro Andrea Gregorio Mattioli was the first to describe the practice of women using *Atropa belladonna* to dilate the pupils of the eyes for cosmetic effect.

PETRVS ANDREAS MATTHIOLVS MEDICVS
Neglectam Medicis damnoso crimine partem
Naturæ pulchra & munera multiplicis,
Andreas dum lustrat agros, dumque vndique quærit,
Admouit chartis lumen Apollineis.
D 8

The specific epithet for the deadly nightshade, *belladonna* ('beautiful lady' in Italian), derives from the effect that the plant has on the eye and its functions. The plant causes the pupil of the eye to dilate due to the effect on the muscle of the iris, and thus it was traditionally used by women as a cosmetic treatment to enhance their attractiveness. Matthiolus (Pietro Andrea Gregorio Mattioli, 1501–1577), a distinguished physician practising in Siena in Italy, wrote *Discorsi*, a great commentary on the botanical works of Dioscorides. He was the first to describe the practice of using deadly nightshade in this way and as a result tincture of *Atropa* became known as 'belladonna'. When the botanist Carl Linnaeus (1707–1778) undertook his formal classification of the plant kingdom in the 1700s, he incorporated both ideas: the generic name *Atropa* (the cutting or deadly Fate) and the species name *belladonna* – an interesting conjunction.

According to folklore, deadly nightshade was an important plant in the pharmacopoeia of witches throughout the late Middle Ages. Although they also used mandrake, henbane and hemlock, *Atropa* was pre-eminent because it was regarded as one of the devil's favourite plants. The story goes that the devil would sprinkle this plant with his own blood every night of the year and would regularly take cuttings for his malign purposes. On only one night of the year – Walpurgis Night, the traditional spring festival celebrated on 30 April – did he neglect his duties, since that night he was busy taking part in Black Mass celebrations.

It was said that witches, believing that the plant had found favour in the eyes of the devil, would use it as a constituent of their 'flying ointments' – hallucinogenic ointments they would apply to help them fly to gatherings with other witches. The usual combination of plants would be nightshade,

Walpurgis Night, the gathering of witches on the Brocken, the highest peak in Germany's Harz mountains, just before May Day, is the one time in the year when the devil is supposedly too busy to attend to his work of sprinkling *Atropa belladonna* with his blood.

A 1677 frontispiece showing the planets instilling poisonous properties into *Atropa* while a man below descends into madness after eating its berries.

hemlock, mandrake and henbane pounded into an ointment with bear's grease.

This was then rubbed into the skin and genitals, causing the witch to experience delusions, hallucinations and sensations of levitation or flying, believed to be the reason why witches are often portrayed as flying on broomsticks. Witches were also said to swallow small amounts of nightshade in order to practise the art of divination, or fortune-telling. Conversely, peasants at this time had a popular superstition that keeping a sprig of deadly nightshade in the house would ward off evil spirits and prevent fiends from attacking their families, homes or livestock.

The Therapeutic Uses of the Plant

Throughout this late medieval period deadly nightshade was largely confined to the secret world of witches, wizards and folk healers.

Then, in the 16th and 17th centuries, herbalists and apothecaries began to embark upon a systematic study of plants both useful and dangerous. Among the first major figures in Britain were the botanists and herbalists John Gerard (1545–1612), Nicholas Culpeper (1616–1664) and John Parkinson (1567–1650). Gerard called the plant 'the lethal *Solanum*' or 'sleepy nightshade'. He recounted three cases of poisoning caused by the berries and instructed the readers of his 1597 *Herball* to banish these pernicious plants from their gardens. Otherwise, he said, women and children would lust after the shining black berries which might seem beautiful but were actually potentially deadly.

Eventually the medicinal uses of the plant began to be investigated and it was soon included in pharmacopoeias and dispensatories. One of the classic descriptions is that by Andrew Duncan (1773–1823) in *The Edinburgh New Dispensatory* of 1803, in which he claimed that *Atropa* could be used to successfully treat several illnesses, particularly the plague, and conditions such as paralysis, epilepsy, whooping cough, melancholy and mania.

Duncan advised that the powdered leaves or root should be used first, and if these failed then an infusion of the plant in warm water could be ingested. The dose of all these preparations was to be gradually increased on a daily basis until 'tension in the throat' developed, at which point it would be imprudent to increase the dose further. He also mentioned that Professor Johann Reimarus (1729–1814), a German physician and natural historian, had used an infusion of *Atropa* to dilate the pupil in order to facilitate the removal of cataracts. This episode marked the beginning of the now commonplace use of pupil-dilating drugs in eye surgery.

From the middle of the 19th century to the late 1950s, belladonna was also incorporated into plasters and liniments. These could be purchased over the counter and were popular

Atropine

In the early 1800s, around the time that Andrew Duncan was compiling his dispensatory in Edinburgh, chemistry began its great leap forward with the work of Sir Humphry Davy (1778–1829) in London and the activities of several French and German chemists. In Paris an assault was made on the plant kingdom and a number of important alkaloids were isolated and characterised, including quinine, morphine and strychnine. Atropine was isolated from the roots of belladonna in 1831 by the German pharmacist Heinrich Mein (1799–1864). In the plant, it occurs as the left-handed variety of the compound, i.e. l-hyoscyamine, but during extraction it partially changes to d-hyoscyamine, the right-handed variety (a process called racemisation). Accordingly, atropine is an equal mixture of the two alkaloids and is properly called dl-hyoscyamine. In structure it is closely related to the alkaloid hyoscine and in many ways their actions are similar.

Atropine

$C_{17}H_{23}NO_3$

Extracts of *Atropa belladonna* were used in plasters and liniments functioning as a painkiller by acting as a counter-irritant.

with the public, as they often saved an expensive visit to the doctor. They were used to treat a wide variety of conditions that caused aches and pains, including neuralgia, rheumatism, lumbago and tuberculosis. The plant alkaloids in the preparations relieved pain through acting as a counter-irritant: they increased blood flow to the skin where they were applied, which generated heat in the area and thus soothed the pain. They were less severe than similar plasters that used the mustard plant (*Brassica juncea* or *B. nigra*). Belladonna was sometimes used in combination with other plants. One example was the plaster that also contained an extract of monkshood (*Aconitum napellus*). This plant produces aconitine, a deadly alkaloid that can cause cardiac and respiratory failure. People were known to purchase this toxic plaster with the aim of using it to commit murder by poisoning. They would steep off the two alkaloids, aconitine and atropine, into water in order to use the resulting poisonous liquid.

The Plant as a Poison

After the pure alkaloid was isolated in 1831, there were – perhaps inevitably – cases of poisoning, either deliberate or accidental. In 1911, the American toxicologist Rudolph Witthaus (1846–1915) reported that he knew of 682 cases of atropine poisoning. Of these, 379 were caused by preparations of belladonna (eye drops, plasters or liniments) and 303 by the pure alkaloid atropine. More than 500 of these poisonings were deemed to be accidental; there were also 37 suicides and 14 murders. There were 60 deaths reported. This was, of course, before the days of intensive care and artificial ventilation and so a number of these deaths would not necessarily occur now. Since then,

atropine poisoning has become rare. Plasters, liniments and eye drops containing atropine have either become obsolete or have been banned altogether. Poisoning now most often occurs when people eat the attractive, and supposedly tasty, black berries of the plant, not realising they are poisonous, but deaths are nonetheless very rare.

It is now much more difficult to obtain supplies of atropine. The drug is largely, if not entirely, found in hospitals, pharmacies, research laboratories and drug companies. As a result, only doctors, anaesthetists, pharmacists and research scientists can obtain the pure alkaloid with relative ease in the course of their daily work.

When atropine is administered in overdose, whether by accident or design, a peculiar conjunction of symptoms results which has been characterised using the following mnemonic: 'Hot as a hare, blind as a bat, dry as a bone, red as a beet and mad as a hen'. When this particular constellation of symptoms is observed, then it becomes

A bottle for tincture of belladonna. Bottles of this type were made with certain textures and colours so that they were easily recognisable as poisonous.

Science Photo Library

The shining black berries of the plant often entice people to eat them and they are said to have a pleasant taste despite being one of the most poisonous parts.

relatively easy to make the correct diagnosis and the only confusion likely to occur is with poisoning by other Solanaceae such as henbane (*Hyoscyamus niger*) or the thorn apple (*Datura stramonium*). Fever is common, particularly in young children. Dilation of the pupils occurs, and the vision may become blurred. An early sign of atropine overdose is profound dryness of the mouth and throat, with severe thirst and difficulty swallowing. Finally, flushing in the face and a general reddening of the skin, caused by the blood vessels dilating, is another common early sign of intoxication.

A person suffering from an atropine overdose may also display symptoms of a mental state resembling mania. Their speech may become incoherent and unintelligible, which, together with an accompanying staggering gait, can make the person appear drunk. They may be restless and agitated, and may complain of hallucinations. The symptoms can be mistaken for those of alcohol withdrawal. Furthermore, atropine often causes a rapid heartbeat and increase in the white cell count, both of which can suggest a viral or bacterial infection, and so a wrong diagnosis can easily be made.

Once it is clear that berries have been ingested and the plant has been identified it is usually fairly easy to diagnose atropine

> No no, go not to Lethe,
> neither twist
> Wolf's-bane, tight rooted,
> for its poisonous wine.
> Nor suffer thy pale forehead
> to be kiss'd
> By nightshade, ruby grape
> of Proserpine.
>
> John Keats, *Ode on Melancholy*

The Edinburgh Poisoner

Although atropine poisoning is now rare, medical staff nonetheless have to be on their guard for symptoms that might be suggestive of this type of intoxication. This is very well illustrated by a 1994 case where a man attempted to poison his wife. One evening, a research scientist and lecturer in biochemistry at an Edinburgh University poured his wife a large gin and tonic. She was unaware that her drink had been spiked with atropine, as the bitter tonic water helped to disguise the equally

The bitterness of quinine in tonic water was a good disguise for the bitter-tasting poison atropine.

bitter alkaloid. Five minutes later, she was complaining of pain in her throat, thirst, nausea, dizziness and visual hallucinations. Although his wife appeared to be seriously ill, the man did not immediately ring the emergency services but left a message on his doctor's answering machine. Fortunately the call was relayed to a locum practitioner who decided to go immediately to the house and also called for an ambulance.

The victim's husband told the paramedics that he suspected that the tonic water his wife had drunk – purchased from a supermarket in Edinburgh – had been contaminated with a poison and handed the bottle over to them. Despite having had ample time to dispose of his wife's drink he did not do so; an ambulance technician insisted on seeing the glass and took its contents away for further analysis. It then transpired that other similar cases had occurred in Edinburgh and the surrounding districts. The police forensic analyst was called out and he identified the poison in the tonic water as atropine.

The following day, the supermarket chain removed all bottles of tonic water from their shelves across the UK. At a press conference, the company said that anyone who had purchased tonic water from the same branch over the previous few weeks should return it. It was later confirmed by the forensic science laboratory that six bottles of tonic water had indeed been spiked with atropine.

posioning and proceed with a suitable course of treatment. However, if the poison has passed through an intermediate animal then diagnosis can be difficult. In one case, meat from cattle and rabbits that had grazed on *Atropa belladonna* proved to be toxic. In another peculiar outbreak, three people were

poisoned by eating honey which, on analysis, was found to contain significant amounts of atropine. In all three instances, the cattle, rabbits and bees were presumably relatively immune to the toxic effect of the alkaloid, and the sweet taste of the honey obviously masked the atropine's bitterness.

When the contaminated bottles of tonic came to light, the victim's husband claimed that someone must have adulterated the bottles and that he and his wife were the victims of a psychopathic poisoner. However, two facts emerged that were extremely damaging to his version of events.

First came the evidence of a part-time shelf stacker at the store. He had observed a man putting bottles back on the shelf containing soft drinks, including tonic water. His description of the man fitted that of the husband perfectly. Security tapes were reviewed and these confirmed that he had indeed been in the store on the day in question.

The second line of evidence was that the concentration of atropine discovered in the gin and tonic was 292 mg per litre, while the bottle of tonic found at the house contained only 103 mg per litre. Allowing for dilution of the tonic by the gin, this led to the inescapable conclusion that someone had added additional atropine to the drink. Additionally the concentrations of atropine in the other contaminated bottles of tonic ranged only from 11 to 74 mg per litre. In summary, all the contaminated bottles of tonic water purchased from the store had much lower concentrations of atropine than that in the gin and tonic.

In his summation, the trial judge described the weight of evidence against the accused as largely circumstantial but nevertheless compelling. The jury agreed with these conclusions and found him guilty of the attempted murder of his wife. He was sentenced to 12 years' imprisonment.

A number of interesting points arise from this case, the first of which is the choice of poison. As a biochemistry lecturer the man knew about the bitter taste of atropine, and so worked out that putting the poison into tonic water – containing bitter quinine – would disguise the taste. He would certainly also have been aware of the fact that atropine had always been very difficult to detect and measure in body fluids and tissues. However, modern techniques of chromatography and mass spectrometry had made it possible to identify and measure minute amounts of atropine.

An average fatal dose of atropine is approximately 100 mg. The victim would therefore have needed to swallow approximately 330 ml of the mixture to receive this dose. She probably ingested no more than 50 mg, sufficient to poison but not to kill her – her would-be poisoner had not fortified the tonic with sufficient extra atropine.

All in all, this was a sophisticated and calculated attempt to poison, backed up by considerable scientific knowledge and experience. But for the miscalculation as to the dose of atropine and his subsequent panic at the scene of the attempted murder, this poisoner might well have succeeded.

What better example could there be to illustrate that properties both therapeutic and toxic can be present in the same plant? The very names deadly nightshade and belladonna are symbols of the dual nature of this species and the way it has been considered as a force for both good and evil. As with many of the plants in this book, the history of *Atropa belladonna* goes right back to its use as a poison in ancient times and then proceeds through centuries of attempts to discover and harness its healing properties before a sharp reminder of its potentially deadly effects was made evident in the 20th century.

Physostigma venenosum Balfour.

2 – The Calabar Bean (*Physostigma venenosum*): An African Ordeal Poison

The unravelling of the properties of *Physostigma venenosum*, the Calabar bean, marked an important moment in medical science. The work on the alkaloid physostigmine contained in the bean unlocked the mysteries of the autonomic nervous system and changed the face of medicine for ever. Many drugs which are used today to treat chronic diseases have as their basis the knowledge catalysed by its discovery. However, its sinister and deadly beginnings in African trials by ordeal still haunt its modern story, as the case study later in the chapter will show.

The major work on the taxonomy of *Physostigma venenosum* was carried out by John Hutton Balfour at the Royal Botanic Garden Edinburgh in the period 1840 to 1860. A climbing vine, the plant is usually found growing up to 10 m tall, generally by the banks of rivers, in countries including Nigeria, Cameroon and Gabon. A member of the hugely diverse pea and bean family Leguminosae/Fabaceae, it has trifoliolate leaves which are reminiscent of those of the creeping beans to which it is related. *Physostigma* is distinguished from similar genera, such as *Macuna* and *Phaseolus*, by characters in its flower, pod and seed. The flowers are particularly distinctive because the stigma ends with a prominent beak-like appendage which was thought to be hollow and which gives the plant its specific epithet (*physo*, from the Greek, means bladder-like). The bean itself is the seed of the plant and is also known as the eséré nut or chop nut; an alternative name for physostigmine is eserine. Its colour ranges from a light coffee to an almost perfect black. The fact that the bean is easily confused with those of other species has led to many cases of accidental poisoning.

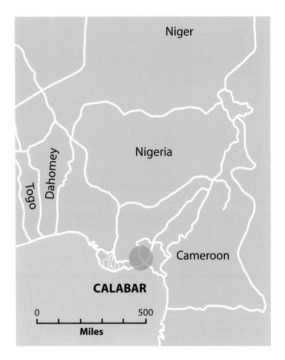

The Calabar Bean: From Africa to Edinburgh

In medieval times, in Britain as well as in the rest of Europe, a person accused of a crime was found innocent or guilty on the basis of a judicial practice known as trial by ordeal. This consisted of making the accused submit to an experience that was at best unpleasant and at worst fatal. The test was usually whether or not the accused would survive the ordeal, with survival or escape from injury taken to mean innocence. The practice was founded on the assumption that God would save the innocent. Trial by ordeal faded out in Europe in the late Middle Ages, although the practice did not disappear completely there until the 16th century.

An Egbo witch doctor from Nigeria. The Egbo were said to have adopted the use of *Physostigma venenosum* in their ordeal trials from their Efik-speaking neighbours.

John Hutton Balfour, Regius Keeper of the Royal Botanic Garden Edinburgh 1845–1879, was the first to describe the plant, which he attempted to grow in the Glasshouses in Edinburgh.

In parts of Africa, however, trial by ordeal persists to this day and is carried out under the supervision of 'witch doctors'. When in the 19th century the missionaries and civil servants of the British Empire reached the coast near the city of Calabar in Nigeria, they found that a particularly vicious form of trial by ordeal was taking place. The chiefs of the Efik tribe subjugated both their own people and their slaves by arbitrarily accusing individuals of being possessed by spirits. Using the seed of the Calabar bean as the ordeal poison, they would administer a dose to the accused. If the victim vomited and did not die, they were regarded as innocent. If they did die they were branded as guilty and convicted of sorcery. The accused's body would be taken into the forest and burnt to allow the evil spirits to return to their natural home.

The Efik hierarchy had very stringent rules with regard to the handling of the beans. Anybody found gathering them at the river bank without the permission of the authorities would be put to death. Similarly, anybody possessing them without the requisite permission would be summarily executed. The missionaries tried to persuade the Efiks to discontinue the practice but to no avail.

As an alternative, the ministers of religion decided to bring some of the beans back to Edinburgh in the hope that they could be cultivated, the poison identified and an antidote developed. These objectives sound straightforward but took another 50 years of unremitting effort. Accordingly, samples of the pods and seeds began to be sent back to Scotland and some came into the hands of John Hutton Balfour (1808–1884), Regius Keeper of the Royal Botanic Garden Edinburgh and Professor of Medicine and Botany at Edinburgh University.

Robert Christison, who was instrumental in establishing toxicology as a branch of medicine, poisoned himself with the bean during his investigations into its effects. Happily his knowledge of poison allowed him to act quickly and employ an emetic to save himself.

Known widely as 'Woody Fibre', a sobriquet bestowed upon him by his students, he was a great innovator. He studied the dried specimens of the ordeal bean which had been brought back from Africa. Deciding that it was a new species, he named it *Physostigma venenosum*.

Balfour planted some of the seeds in the Glasshouses at the Garden. A few germinated but did not flower and so no beans were available with which to conduct experiments. The head gardener did notice, however, that one of the plants had been attacked by a snail which had then died, confirming that *Physostigma* was indeed poisonous, at least to molluscs. It appears that Balfour then gave up further attempts to cultivate the plant. Another player then entered the scene: toxicologist Robert Christison (1797–1882). Christison held several professorships at Edinburgh University, including that of Materia Medica. He had a deep and abiding interest in poisons and had worked on hemlock (*Conium maculatum*), laburnum (*Laburnum anagyroides*) and hemlock water dropwort (*Oenanthe crocata*). He was also an authority on arsenic and had written extensively on the subject. Hearing of Balfour's failed attempts to cultivate the bean he decided to obtain some for his own study, with a view to isolating the poison and determining its mode of action. He started his experiments on rabbits but obtained markedly inconsistent results. This was probably due to the fact that the amount of poison in a single bean could vary widely due to seasonal effects and loss of toxicity during storage and transport.

Dissatisfied, Christison opted to take the bean himself. After one unsuccessful attempt he took a higher 'dose' and subsequently became violently ill, nearly fainted and began to salivate profusely. His heart started beating rapidly. Fortunately he was able to swallow shaving water. The soap in the water caused him to vomit immediately and this probably saved his life. He did not try the experiment again; instead, he made many attempts to isolate the poison but they all failed. He did, however, conclude that it was probably an alkaloid.

The beans of *Physostigma venenosum* were used in ordeal trials; they were often ground and made into a drink for the accused.

Science Photo Library

Physostigmine

Thomas Richard Fraser (1841–1920) and his colleague Alexander Crum Brown (1838–1922), Professor of Chemistry at Edinburgh University, were the first to isolate an impure poison from the bean. They identified it as a base which they would be able to use in order to form salts of the alkaloid with salicylic acid and bromic acids. The first people to isolate the alkaloid itself were the German chemists Julius von Jobst (1839–1920) and Oswald Hesse (1835–1917) in 1863. Shortly afterwards, using the pure alkaloid, Fraser and Crum Brown were able to prove that physostigmine was an antidote to the poisonous alkaloid atropine derived from deadly nightshade (*Atropa belladonna*) (see Chapter 1). A very important question remained: how did physostigmine and atropine exert their specific and opposing effects on the body? Fraser tentatively

Physostigmine (also known as eserine)

$$CH_{15}H_{21}N_3O_2$$

suggested that the two alkaloids would bind to the 'proteinaceous' substances in the body and that atropine could displace physostigmine from this binding substance and vice versa.

However, it was not until the first half of the following century that the question was fully answered. English pharmacologist Henry Hallett Dale (1875–1968) and his

Thomas Richard Fraser isolated the active substance from the beans and, after his investigations, recommended it be used in ophthalmology.

The Wider Significance

Founded in 1726, the University of Edinburgh's Medical School was considered one of the world's foremost medical institution almost from its inception through to the 19th century and beyond. Oxford and Cambridge were in these early years only open to communicant members of the Anglican church and neither London University nor the great provincial universities of England had fully developed faculties of medicine until some years later. Edinburgh's teaching model was based on those of the University of Padua in Italy, founded in the 16th century, and the 17th-century University of Leiden in the Netherlands. As a consequence Edinburgh attracted many students from all parts of Britain, North America and the colonies, which in turn had a positive effect on the city's economy.

A major part in the discovery, classification and elucidation of the Calabar bean was played

Henry Hallett Dale (left) who, with his colleague
Otto Loewi (right), was awarded the Nobel Prize for
Physiology or Medicine for their discovery of acetycholine.

German-born colleague Otto Loewi (1873–
1961) knew that there were two opposing
parts in the automatic nervous system: the
sympathetic (activated by adrenaline) and the
parasympathetic (activated by an unknown
transmitter). Dale had suggested in 1912
that this parasympathetic transmitter was

perhaps acetylcholine, but he had no
evidence to prove his case. Meanwhile Loewi
had suggested that the parasympathetic
transmitter at the cardiac nerve endings
was acetylcholine. Then, in 1934, Dale and
his colleagues showed that the mystery
substance released from neurones in the neck
and at the voluntary muscle nerve endings
was indeed acetylcholine. It was discovered
that this transmitter at the nerve endings,
heart and gut was preserved from enzymic
destruction by physostigmine. This property
of physostigmine would prove essential to its
use in treatment of myasthenia gravis – an
autoimmune disease causing chronic muscle
weakness – as well as other neurological
disorders. The pharmacological world was set
ablaze by this discovery and Dale and Loewi
were jointly awarded the Nobel Prize in 1936
for their identification of acetylcholine.

by three men at the Edinburgh Medical School:
the aforementioned John Hutton Balfour and
Robert Christison, together with physician
and pharmacologist Thomas Richard Fraser,
who was both Professor of Medicine and later
Dean of the Medical Faculty. Their authority
was such that both Christison and Fraser could
claim to be the fathers of modern pharmacology,
toxicology and therapeutics.

One of the linchpins of the tremendous
advances made in these subjects during the
19th century was the Calabar bean, which
would prove to be an essential tool in unlocking
the mysteries of the autonomic nervous
system. It is safe to say that without this
seemingly insignificant bean our knowledge
of this vital bodily system would have been
delayed for a considerable time to come.

Alexander Crum Brown who, with his colleague
Thomas Richard Fraser, was the first to isolate poison
from the bean.

The Miracle at St Alfege's

In 1934, a little-known hospital called St Alfege's in Greenwich, London, was an unexpected source of the development in the therapeutic uses of physostigmine. Dr Mary Walker (1888–1974) worked at this hospital as a senior house officer and had developed a particular interest in myasthenia gravis. She became convinced that the drooping of the eyelid, double vision and muscular weakness symptomatic of this disorder were similar to the effects of curare poisoning (see Chapter 7). Myasthenia gravis might therefore be caused by a curare-like substance circulating in the blood of these patients. Knowing that in experiments on animals, physostigmine had been shown to reverse the effects of curare on muscles, she decided to administer physostigmine to a woman with severe myasthenia.

Within minutes of receiving the injection, the patient lifted her head, her double vision cleared and muscular power returned to her arms and legs. The effects were considered nothing short of miraculous: patients responded readily to small doses of physostigmine and showed sustained improvement in both their vision and their muscular power. Knowing of Henry Hallett Dale's suggestion in 1912, Walker argued that physostigmine was acting to prevent the destruction of acetylcholine at the junction

Dr Mary Walker who first successfully used physostigmine in the treatment of myasthenia gravis after noticing the similarities of the disease's symptoms to those of curare poisoning, which physostigmine was known to counteract.

between the nerve and the muscle as it had been shown to do at the cardiac nerve endings by Loewi. This pioneering work paved the way for the use of other similar drugs in the treatment and diagnosis of myasthenia gravis and significantly improved patients' quality of life.

When Christison and Fraser carried out their research on *Physostigma* and physostigmine in the 19th century, it was always their hope that a therapeutic use would be found for the poisonous alkaloid. Their aspirations have surely been fulfilled in the treatment of myasthenia gravis. Even more importantly, perhaps, the availability of physostigmine led Dale and Loewi to the identification of acetylcholine, the hitherto unrecognised transmitter in the nervous system. The ramifications of this discovery are incalculable; since then thousands of scientific papers in the field of pharmacology have described the use of this compound as a primary investigative tool. We must also acknowledge the initial tentative efforts of John Hutton Balfour at RBGE, where he set the whole saga in motion when he acted on the stories emerging from West Africa and attempted to cultivate the bean. It was Pliny the Elder who coined the epithet *Ex Africa semper aliquid novi* – out of Africa there is always something new. We could not find a more striking example that fulfils this aphorism than the history of the ordeal bean of Calabar.

The Torso in the Thames

Although authorities in West Africa have tried to ban the use of the Calabar bean, certain 'witch doctors' still persist in the illegal use of this poison. Modern use does not seem to be related to trial by ordeal but to ritual sacrifice. The standard practice in ritual sacrifice is to decapitate a goat and then sprinkle the blood issuing from the neck onto a person, an object or the ground in order to appease the gods. In the following tragic case, the victim subjected to the ritual was not a goat but a young boy. On 21 September 2001 a body was pulled by the police from the river Thames near Tower Bridge. It was almost immediately apparent that the body was a headless torso from which all four limbs had been removed. The victim appeared to be a boy of African or Afro-Caribbean origin, between five and ten years of age. The police gave the boy the provisional name of Adam.

Many months of detailed forensic investigation followed. The post mortem suggested that the neck had been severed while the boy was still alive and all four limbs removed after death. Analysis of the strontium and carbon present in the boy's bones strongly suggested that he had originated from the Benin City area of Nigeria. The contents of his intestine included plant material that was shown to be the residue of the Calabar bean, a substance commonly available to the local doctors in Nigeria.

Detectives working in Nigeria eventually established that he was probably an eight-year-old who had disappeared in the year 2000 from his home. It appeared that he had been abducted from Nigeria and brought to London to become a victim of ritual sacrifice. He had been prepared for this terrible ordeal by being administered the Calabar bean, which would have partially paralysed the skeletal muscles and rendered him less able to resist the violent attack that followed.

Tower Bridge on the Thames in London where the body of Adam was recovered by police. Tests showed that the boy had been partially paralysed with *Physostigma venenosum*.

Solaneae.

Hyoscyamus niger L.

WM.

3 – Henbane (*Hyoscyamus niger*): Hyoscine and Hawley Harvey Crippen

The dark side of henbane has been known since ancient times, although, like many of the plants included in this book, it has also made a significant contribution to medical knowledge. The Greeks regarded it as a symbol of what awaited them in Hades, while William Shakespeare, in *Hamlet*, talks of the 'juice of cursed hebenon', widely thought to be henbane, that killed Hamlet's father King Claudius. Despite this, its many medicinal virtues have been mentioned in ancient Greek pharmacopeias and later in medieval Anglo-Saxon texts, setting the scene for the eventual work by 19th- and 20th-century pharmacists to isolate the active principle and bring its therapeutic benefits into a modern context.

Henbane (*Hyoscyamus niger*), also known as the stinking nightshade, is a member of the Solanaceae family, allied to tobacco, the potato and the tomato. It is a foul-smelling annual or biennial herb which grows up to 80 cm high. The generic name is derived from the Greek *hyos* (pig) and *kyamos* (bean), suggesting that pigs may consume it safely, and the species name from the Latin *niger* (black). Its flowers vary from yellow to dull green with purple veins. Indigenous to temperate Eurasia, it has been naturalised in other parts of Europe and North America. Another relative, *Hyoscyamus albus*, occurs widely in southern Europe and has bell-shaped white flowers. The characteristic foul smell of the genus is produced by the compound tetrahydroputrescine, which is reminiscent of rotting flesh and probably acts to attract pollinating insects.

The History of Henbane

Henbane was well known to the Greeks and Romans and recognised as being potent and poisonous. In the ancient myths of Greece it was believed that some of the souls of the dead roamed the banks of the river Styx at the entrance to Hades, the underworld. These wraith-like spirits wore garlands of henbane to warn the living of what awaited them in the kingdom of the dead. Dioscorides (c. AD 40–90), the Greek physician and botanist, recognised

Science Photo Library

Scenes of levitation from Joseph Glanvill's, *Saducismus triumphatus*: or, *Full and plain evidence concerning witches and apparitions* of 1681. Witches used henbane, amongst other ingredients, in the ointments which supposedly gave them the power of flight.

THE COUNTRY TOOTH DRAWER.
Printed and Published by W. Davison Alnwick.

An engraving of a 'country puller'; the seeds of henbane were often used to temporarily dull the pain of toothache by travelling quacks.

however that, as long as great care was taken, the plant could be used in the treatment of pain and insomnia. Some decades previously, Aulus Cornelius Celsus (c. 25 BC–AD 50), the Roman author of the medical treatise *De Medicina*, had developed an oily salve that could be rubbed into the skin, which proved to be a much safer way to administer the plant than orally. It also proved effective as a local anaesthetic.

Much later, in medieval times, witches would gather plants and other material from hedgerows and use them for various purposes, including making broomsticks. An ash handle protected the witch from drowning and the birch twigs of the brush bound evil spirits together. The twigs were held together by strips of willow, as this latter tree was sacred to Hecate, the goddess of witchcraft. Hecate was also thought to 'own' certain plants such as henbane, belladonna and mandrake. Armed with her broomstick, the witch would burn

henbane and inhale the fumes, which would conjure up the spirits or demons and enable her to carry out spells, incantations and magical acts. Such were its hallucinogenic properties that she would have the sensation of flying through the air and levitating.

There was widespread interest in the plants used in witchcraft. Henbane in particular had two main medicinal uses: the treatment of toothache and neuralgia and the development of the soporific sponge. In the Middle Ages fairs were a prominent feature of town and village life. A popular figure at such gatherings was the travelling quack, or mountebank, who claimed to be able to cure toothache and other painful conditions. He would take the seeds of henbane and char or steam them in an oven. The sufferer would then be instructed to inhale the smoke or fumes. Hyoscine, the active ingredient of henbane, would act as an analgesic and temporarily assuage the pain.

The herbalist John Gerard (1545–1612), in his *Herball* of 1597, noted that the 'drawers of teeth' pretended to cause worms to appear from the offending molars.[1] In fact, the seeds of the plant discharged their small white embryos when heated, which were the 'worms' held to be responsible for the toothache. By the time the narcotic effect of the hyoscine had worn off and the pain had returned, the travelling trickster had moved on to the next fair. As late as the 19th century some country folk still smoked henbane in a similar way to tobacco to relieve the pain of toothache.

The most common form of anaesthesia in the Middle Ages and beyond was the soporific sponge, developed by the Salerno school of medicine, Europe's leading medical institution, and based on early Arabic methods of anaesthesia by inhalation. A sponge would be soaked in a mixture of herbs and allowed to dry. When needed, it would be rehydrated by soaking it in hot water and held under the patient's nose. The patient would then inhale the vapour and be rendered unconscious. The preparation contained an infusion of henbane, the opium poppy (*Papaver somniferum*) and mandrake (*Mandragora officinalis*), all of which had a narcotic effect and could induce a state of unconsciousness that lasted for several hours. Its effects, however, were unpredictable as the potency of the plants used to prepare the ingredients for the sponge varied and there was no way of measuring the dose. Sometimes it did not work well at all and had to be supplemented with alcoholic spirits; on other occasions, it worked too well and the patient never regained consciousness. The French physician Guy de Chauliac (1300–1368) described the soporific sponge in *Chirurgia Magna*, his surgical textbook, but warned that it could be dangerous as breathing might be affected and death could occur. Despite this, it continued to be used regularly as a method of anaesthesia until the 17th century.

By the 18th and 19th centuries surgeons were instead relying on physically restraining the patient and perfecting lightning-fast technique, such as amputating a leg in just a few minutes. By 1850, the soporific sponge had been replaced by ether and chloroform for inhalational anaesthesia and became largely an object of historical curiosity. It enjoyed a minor revival in 1847, however, when a Dr Dauriol, a physician from Toulouse, reintroduced it. In that year he published a paper in which he described his attempts to find a substitute for the anaesthetic ether.[2] Henbane was among the plants he used in his soporific sponge; the others included *Solanum nigrum* (black nightshade) and *Datura stramonium* (thorn apple). Unfortunately, Dauriol's sponge suffered from the same drawback as its earlier equivalent and it did not gain wide acceptance.

In large doses henbane is deadly and it has been used both as a criminal poison and

A portrait of Catherine Monvoisin or 'La Voisin', known for her involvement in the *affaire des poisons* and subsequently sentenced to death for witchcraft and poisoning. She had made use of henbane in her activities.

Hyoscine

The problem with henbane and other Solanaceae was that different plants from different sources varied widely in their pharmacological effects and toxicity. Moreover, no one knew why the plants behaved as they did and caused certain physiological effects and not others. French and German chemists began to make progress in solving this problem at the beginning of the 19th century. The first major breakthrough was achieved in 1831 when the German pharmacist Heinrich Mein (1799–1864) isolated the alkaloid atropine from *Atropa belladonna* (see Chapter 1). However, henbane seemed to have certain properties that were different from those of atropine. In particular, it caused sedation more regularly and reliably than atropine. It was suspected that there was another alkaloid in henbane and eventually another German pharmacist, Albert Ladenburg (1842–1911), working at the University of

Kiel, isolated hyoscine in 1880. He also showed that the only chemical difference between hyoscine and atropine was that hyoscine had one additional oxygen atom.

To complicate matters further, during the previous century Giovanni Scopoli (1723–1788), an Austrian-Italian botanist and physician, had conducted research into a plant (later named *Scopolia carniolica*) indigenous to what is now Slovenia and had shown that it too was a rich source of tropane alkaloids. One of these became known as scopolamine, but it is in fact identical to hyoscine. In American sources and research papers, the term scopolamine is still used in favour of hyoscine.

The mystery of how hyoscine worked continued to go unsolved until the 1930s, when the English pharmacologist Henry Hallett Dale (1875–1968) and his colleagues isolated the neurotransmitter acetylcholine from the voluntary muscle nerve endings, following Otto Loewi's isolation of the identical

Stirling Tolbooth Jail where henbane seeds were found during renovations.

© Crown Copyright: RCAHMS. Licensor www.rcahms.gov.uk

as a means of execution in the penal system. Among the most notorious examples were seen in what was known as *l'affaire des poisons* (the affair of the poisons), a major scandal that occurred in the highest ranks of French society from 1677 to 1682, during the reign of King Louis XIV. During this time a number of aristocrats were poisoned and other members of the royal court accused of being responsible for their deaths. Louis XIV, fearful for his own life, set up a *chambre ardente* (a type of court usually held to try heretics) to investigate the deaths, many of which were caused by the nightshade alkaloids. Over the next few years, nearly 400 people were investigated, 36 of whom were sentenced to death for witchcraft and poisoning. The most famous poisoner of the period was Catherine Monvoisin, who was substance at the heart. It became apparent that both hyoscine and atropine blocked the action of acetylcholine at these nerve endings, and so the puzzle was finally solved.

Hyoscine often occurs as a mixture of the right-handed 'd' and left-handed 'l' forms but only the 'l' form is pharmacologically active. L-hyoscine became generally available in the first decade of the 20th century and it is interesting to examine the pharmacopoeias of that time to see what preparations were in use. *Hyoscyami folia* (henbane leaves) are mentioned, although these were going out of fashion in favour of pure l-hyoscine. Hyoscine hydrobromide and hyoscine sulphate were the recommended preparations, used to treat mania and Parkinson's disease. They were also used as pre-medication before surgical anaesthesia and to produce a state of sedation known as 'twilight sleep', used to relieve pain in childbirth. The melting point (one of the defining properties of any chemical compound and a measure

Hyoscine

6,7-Epoxytropine tropate; Scopolamine

(−)-form

$CH_{17}H_{21}NO_4$

of purity) of l-hyoscine was confirmed as 193°C. This, as we shall see below, became a central point in the prosecution's evidence during the trial of Dr Crippen.

convicted of witchcraft and burned in 1680. Her poisons of choice had been henbane, thorn apple, Spanish fly and arsenic. With her execution the scandalous episode finally drew to a close.

Other users of henbane were jailers and executioners. Sixteenth-century accounts from Lucerne in Switzerland show that the town executioner there purchased henbane seeds. Closer to home, in 2002 dozens of henbane seeds were found preserved in clay when the 17th-century Tolbooth Jail in Stirling was being excavated for renovation work. Whether the seeds were used to subdue violent prisoners or to sedate them before hanging or execution remains unknown. However, these discoveries illustrate how widespread the use of henbane has been throughout history.

Nowadays, hyoscine barely receives a mention in the *British National Formulary* and similar pharmacological reference books. It is used to prevent seasickness and in palliative care to suppress hypersalivation, but has few other uses. However, as can be seen from the account of the Dr Crippen case, it is deserving of its status as a landmark drug. Together with atropine and physostigmine, hyoscine was instrumental in unravelling the secrets of the autonomic nervous system. Later, the use of hyoscine as a poison in the case of Dr Crippen led to a breakthrough in the development of British forensic science. Thus its dual facets of healing and killing have served to further modern science significantly.

The Infamous Case of Hawley Harvey Crippen

The Dr Crippen murder case was among the most significant early examples of how forensic sciences could be used to establish cause of death. The case and subsequent trial would bring hyoscine to worldwide prominence.

Hawley Harvey Crippen was born in Coldwater, Michigan in 1862. He obtained a diploma in homoeopathic medicine and later another qualification from the Ophthalmic Hospital in New York. He was never awarded a medical degree but always referred to himself as 'Dr Crippen', as it was good for business. At first, he wandered from state to state practising his medical arts in a number of the larger cities. After his first wife died suddenly, he became involved with, and subsequently married, a 17-year-old would-be singer and dancer whose real name was Kunigunde Mackamotski, although she went by the name of Cora Turner for her stage appearances.

In 1900, Crippen decided to move to Britain and became the manager of a pharmaceutical medicines retailer in London. Cora Crippen eventually joined him in England where she hoped to become an opera singer. Prone to rather extravagant behaviour, she reportedly entertained a number of male friends and adopted a lavish lifestyle. Although Crippen lived a quiet and abstemious life he was constantly short of money as a result of Cora's spendthrift habits.

The famous tragedy began when the Crippens moved to 39 Hilldrop Crescent in London and Crippen began an affair with his secretary, Ethel Le Neve. In December 1909, Cora found out about these liaisons and threatened to leave her husband.

Bridgeman Images

Dr Crippen's wife and victim Cora Crippen, seen here in her guise as Cora Turner, also known as Belle Elmore.

On 15 December, she gave notice to the bank that she wished to withdraw her savings. A month later, on 15 January 1910, Crippen ordered 5 grains (325 mg) of hyoscine hydrobromide from a pharmacy, collecting it a few days later. On 31 January, two guests came to dinner at Hilldrop Crescent: a retired music hall performer called Paul Martinetti and his wife Clara. The guests departed after midnight, after which Cora Crippen was never seen alive again.

The following day, Crippen took a diamond ring and earrings to the pawnbroker and received £80 for them. That same day, Ethel Le Neve moved into

The arrest of Dr Crippen, led from the SS *Montrose* by Inspector Walter Dew who narrowly beat him in the race across the Atlantic.

number 39. Mrs Crippen purportedly wrote to resign her position as treasurer of the Music Hall Ladies' Guild, intimating that she had to leave for America because a relative was ill. This letter was later shown to have been a forgery. A month later, Crippen reported that his wife had died suddenly and had been cremated. A friend of Cora Crippen, a Mr Nash, went to America to try and verify this information but met with no success. When he questioned Crippen on his return, he found him evasive and hesitant. The police were summoned. On his first interview with Crippen, Chief Inspector Dew of Scotland Yard was completely taken in when Crippen claimed that his wife had left him on 1 February and that he had been too

Betrayed by lingerie: Dr Crippen, with a scarf around his face, is led from the liner 'Montrose' by Inspector Dew, July 1910   DAILY MIRROR

THE
LONDON MURDER
MYSTERY.

Mutilated Body found in a Cellar

Arrest of Crippen & Le Neve On board S.S. Montrose

THE NAUGHTY DOCTOR
The Crippen Diary.

embarrassed to admit it. Dew made an initial search of the house but found nothing incriminating. Shortly after he departed, Crippen and Le Neve made a bolt for it, going first to Antwerp by cross-Channel steamer and from there embarking for Canada on the SS *Montrose*.

On learning of the couple's disappearance, Dew ransacked the house at Hilldrop Crescent and dug over the garden. On the third day of the search Dew was exploring the coal cellar with a poker and turned over a few bricks. There, buried in lime, was a body that would prove to be the remains of Cora Crippen. En route to Canada, Captain Kendall of the SS *Montrose* had been alerted, via wireless

An Edwardian flyer informing the public of the latest updates in the Crippen case. Public interest in the murder was unprecedented and continues to this day.

The Infamous Case of Hawley Harvey Crippen

telegraph, of the worldwide search for Dr Crippen and Miss Le Neve and he became suspicious about two of his passengers. One resembled Dr Crippen although he had grown a beard, while the other claimed to be an adolescent boy, but never left his cabin. On 25 July, Captain Kendall sent a telegram to Scotland Yard to say that he was convinced that the circulated description of Crippen fitted his passenger 'Mr Robinson' and that this man spoke with an American accent.

Fortunately the *Montrose* was a fairly slow ship; Dew and his officers went immediately to Liverpool and sailed on the much faster *Laurentic* bound for Quebec in Canada. The national papers plotted the estimated positions of the two ships on a daily basis, arousing great excitement among the general public. The *Laurentic* arrived in Quebec a day earlier than the *Montrose*. Dew and his officers boarded the *Montrose* when it landed, and the suspicious couple were arrested and positively identified as Crippen and Le Neve. They were brought back to London to stand trial. But for the prompt action of Captain Kendall, the couple would have disappeared into the depths of North America and may never have been seen again. The pursuit and arrest of the pair of fugitives captured the public's imagination and the trial at the Old Bailey in London was eagerly awaited and widely reported.

When the remains of the body were removed from the cellar at Hilldrop Crescent the investigators, Dr William Willcox, a Home Office toxicologist, and Dr Bernard Spilsbury, a pathologist, faced a number of significant difficulties. There was no head, limbs or genitals, nor any long bones. Some of the internal organs had been removed, although fortunately not the liver. This made it difficult to establish whether the body was that of a

MARCH 14, 1928.]   PUNCH, OR THE LONDON CHARIVARI.   305

SIR **BERNARD SPILSBURY.**

When arsenic has closed your eyes,
This certain hope your corpse may rest in :—
Sir B. will kindly analyse
The contents of your large intestine.

MR. PUNCH'S PERSONALITIES.—LXIV.

Sir Bernard Spilsbury, the famous forensic pathologist.

woman or a man. The case for the defence was based on the argument that the body had been buried in the cellar before the Crippens bought the house and could have been anyone, man or woman. The prosecution was faced therefore with two key tasks: could they prove beyond reasonable doubt that the body was that of Cora Crippen and could they show that she had been murdered, and if so, by what means?

In the modern era, DNA evidence would have settled the first question promptly and without difficulty. In 1910, Mrs Crippen's identity was proved by a scar on the abdomen which corresponded to her medical history. To convince the jury, Spilsbury brought a microscope into court to demonstrate the changes in the microscopic structure of the tissues – almost certainly the first time this had been done in a British court of law. Willcox carried out an analysis of the hyoscine levels of the stomach contents and those in the intestines, kidneys and liver. The total amount of the alkaloid recovered from all these organs was 18.5 mg, which would correspond to a total amount in the body of 32.5 mg. This compares with an average lethal dose of 8 to 10 mg and would have certainly been sufficient to cause death. Moreover, Willcox was able to obtain a crystalline preparation of the poisonous alkaloid from the pooled organ material. He then showed that this pure specimen had a melting point of 193°C; this figure corresponded to the scientifically established melting point of l-hyoscine.

This demonstration was again a first for forensic science. The final piece of incontrovertible evidence was produced when Willcox took some of the pooled hyoscine extracted from the liver and instilled it into the eye of the St Mary's Hospital cat. The cat's pupil dilated immediately, proving that this was a tropane alkaloid. Other tests demonstrated that the alkaloid was hyoscine rather than the closely related atropine. Willcox also said that, in his opinion, the poison had been given orally and that its bitter taste could have been disguised by an alcoholic drink.

The final argument in the case for the defence collapsed when it was established that underneath the corpse was a pyjama jacket which had been delivered to Hilldrop Crescent in January 1909 when the Crippens were already living there. The prosecuting counsel put the argument to the jury: who could have buried the corpse in that particular jacket? Who was living in the house between January 1909 and January 1910? Only one of the Crippens or a servant. Who was missing and could have been buried in that self-same jacket? Only Cora Crippen. In the face of this barrage of evidence, histological, toxicological and circumstantial, the case for the defence collapsed. When the jury retired, they obviously found the combined weight of the evidence overwhelming. Within half an hour they returned a verdict of guilty and Crippen was sentenced to death; Ethel Le Neve had been charged as an accessory after the fact but was acquitted. The Crippen case was a landmark in the history of British forensic science and became a benchmark for the future. It also established Bernard Spilsbury as the leading forensic pathologist of the day.

DR. CRIPPEN AND MISS LE NEVE.

Dr Crippen and Ethel Le Neve in the dock.

XVIII,1.

70. Hypericaceae.

314. *Hypericum perforatum L.*

Johanniskraut.

4 – St John's Wort (*Hypericum perforatum*): Balm of Hurt Minds

In the Christian tradition, those with mental illnesses were thought to be possessed by an evil spirit. This is well illustrated by the parable of the Gadarene swine in which Jesus cast the demons out of the man who was tormented and 'they entered into the swine and the herd ran violently down a steep place into the lake and were choked'.[1] The man recovered at once and went on his way rejoicing.

As a consequence of this widely held belief it was common practice to wear charms or amulets to ward off demonic assault and possession. Certain plants also came to be regarded as effective at either driving devils out or preventing them from entering in the first place and taking possession of the soul. In this category one plant that was highly prized was St John's wort. Over a number of years St John's wort has received serious consideration as a treatment for depression and attempts have been made to characterise its main active principles and determine how they influence the brain in order to produce beneficial therapeutic effects.

The genus *Hypericum* belongs to the family Hypericaceae and contains approximately 370 species. Members of the genus have opposite leaves dotted with black glands. Typical flowers bear five sepals, five yellow petals and stamens collected into five bundles. The word *Hypericum* is derived from the Greek *hyper* (above) and *eikon* (image), from the popular custom of hanging various species of this genus above holy pictures to repel the devil. Well-known examples include *H. calycinum* (Rose of Sharon or Aaron's beard) from south-east Europe and *H. perforatum* (St John's wort or the Klamath weed) from northern Europe. In the latter the leaves appear peppered with small holes when held up to the light; hence the name *perforatum* (perforated). Common St John's wort grows in woodland, grassland and hedgerows throughout Europe, except in the far north, where it is replaced by the similar but imperforate *H. maculatum*. The plant usually forms a clump or patch with many rounded stems coming from a spreading underground root system.

The History of St John's Wort

The medical effects of this plant have been known since Greek and Roman times and were mentioned by the physicians Hippocrates (460–377 BC), Pliny (AD 23–79) and Dioscorides (c. AD 40–90), who prescribed it as a treatment for wounds, fever and pain. In pagan rituals, the flame-like buds were thought to signify the gift of fire from the gods. These were often burnt as one of the rituals of Beltane, the Celtic fire festival held on 1 May in order to confer a celestial blessing on the sowing of the crops. Later in the year, around the summer solstice on 21 June, bundles of the plant were set alight and dragged across the fields to increase the yield from the crops.

When Christianity arrived in northern Europe, the new faith took over local customs and beliefs and changed them for its own purposes. St John's wort was named after St John the Baptist by these early Christians, as it reaches full bloom in mid-June, coinciding with the saint's feast day on the 24th of that month. Its five yellow petals are said to look like St John's halo, while the red spots that appear on the flowers and leaves in August are symbolic of his blood, as he was beheaded in that month on the orders of King Herod.

St John's Day takes place just a few days after the summer solstice, a significant time for rites involving planting and fertility. In the Hanover region of Germany, another traditional ritual would see Christians go out on the morning of St John's Day and collect from *Hypericum* plants an insect, *Coccus polonica*, which resembled a drop of blood. They believed that this insect had been created to keep alive the memory of the murder of St John the Baptist. It was common lore that the insect could only be encountered on this one day.

Over the years the names of several other saints have been associated with the *Hypericum* plant. *H. tetrapterum* is commonly known as St Peter's wort, while in Gaelic

the many names for *H. perforatum* include 'Virgin Mary's herb' and 'the armpit package of Columba', as a sprig of the plant was traditionally sewn into the armpit of clothing. St Columba was said to carry it with him when he travelled as a missionary; it was believed that he had a special affection for it because of its association with St John the Baptist, whom he deeply revered.

As a result of its association with the saints and its supposed ability to exorcise or ward off evil spirits, the plant came to be known as *Fuga demonum* (repulsor of demons) or devil's scourge. In due course it began to be associated with the healing of wounds. The herbalist John Gerard (1545–1612) noted in his *Herball* of 1597 that St John's wort was 'a most precious remedy for deep wounds, those that are thorow the body … or any wound with a venomed weapon'. He recommended that the leaves, flowers and seeds be stamped

John the Baptist preaching; his association with the plant is thought to be due to its time of flowering and the resemblance of its flower to his halo.

or pressed, immersed in olive oil and set in the hot sun, where they would make an oil the colour of blood. The resulting infused oil would 'provoke urine and be right good against the stone in the bladder'. Because of these healing properties, the plant was known by names such as 'touch-and-heal' or 'balm of the warrior's wound'.

St John's wort doth charm all witches away
If gathered at midnight on the saint's holy day.
Any devils and witches have no power to harm
Those that gather the plant for a charm.
Rub the lintels with that red juicy flower;
No thunder nor tempest will then have the power
To hurt or hinder your house; and bind
Round your neck a charm of similar kind.

From an anonymous 14th-century manuscript

All manner of ailments and conditions were said to respond to *Hypericum*, including bronchitis, haemorrhoids, burns, ulcers and urinary tract infections; by the end of the 18th century it had become something of a panacea. It is thought that in North America a related *Hypericum* species was used by the Iroquois tribe to treat fever and as a fertility aid, and by the Cherokee for diarrhoea, venereal sores and snakebites. This is an interesting example of the emergence of common traditions in widely dispersed cultures.

Helping the Disordered Mind

Even in the 18th century, *Hypericum* was not merely being used to treat physical ailments; it was also recommended as a treatment for illnesses of the mind. Symptoms of supposed demonic possession included low spirits and a depressive mood. As traditional healers were using St John's wort to expel the evil spirits, it was assumed that when the sufferer's mood lifted, this was a sign that the exorcism had been a success. Later, when the plant was being used as a treatment for wounds, burns and minor infections, the antidepressant properties of *Hypericum* soon became clear and it was suggested that it helped people suffering from various depressive ailments. Herbalists in the 19th and early 20th centuries recommended the plant for depression, mania, anxiety and fatigue, without any definite scientific support for their opinions. German herbalists had a particular enthusiasm for *Hypericum* and were said to have maintained a keen interest in St John's wort. Known in Germany as *Johanniskraut* (John's plant), it was prescribed widely for nervous disability of all kinds.

As a result of the widespread use of the plant in Germany and many published reports, the German government decided to investigate its benefits more systematically. In 1978 it gathered together a group of experts (known collectively as Commission E) to report on the various preparations that were available for the treatment of depression. They concluded that *Hypericum* was indeed effective in mild and moderate depression and that the active principle was most likely to be hypericin. As a result of this positive endorsement, the use of St John's wort as a treatment for depression grew in popularity in Germany throughout the 1980s and 1990s until more than three million doses of it were being prescribed annually. Many physicians in Germany still use herbal medicines such as *Hypericum* as a first preference for treating depression, only resorting to the more commonly prescribed synthetic antidepressants when St John's wort appears to have failed.

The major problem with herbal preparations, apart from standardisation, is the multiplicity of active compounds present in varied concentrations in leaves, stems and flowers. Any or all of these compounds might act either to strengthen or to inhibit the effect of another and so there is no substitute for

SPOONER'S MAGIC Nº7.

I feel a fit o' them curst Blue Devils coming across me again

A coloured lithograph depicting a wretched man with impending depression, represented as small demons or devils.

laborious and painstaking controlled clinical trials of the pure chemical entities. One of the difficulties that has stood in the way of St John's wort and its development is the wide variation in the potency of extracts taken from the plant. In order to meet this problem Lichtwer Pharma, a manufacturer of standardised herbal supplements in Germany, introduced in 1992 a high-strength preparation containing 300 mg of hypericin per capsule or tablet. The extract is analysed and then adjusted so that it uniformly contains 0.3% of hypericin. With this carefully standardised extract it has been possible to conduct trials in the United Kingdom and America which in general have supported the earlier German work. The setting of such standards is a very definite advance, but the plant contains many other active compounds, some of which may be more important than hypericin. Other compounds that have been isolated from the plant and identified include pseudohypericin, hyperforin, biapigenin, 2-methylbutanol and gamma-amino butyric acid (GABA). These compounds have been described variously as having sedative, antidepressant, antibacterial and antiviral activity.

In 1996, *Hypericum* came to the attention of the official medical establishment in the United Kingdom, almost two decades later than it had in Germany. In an editorial in the *British Medical Journal*, St John's wort was reviewed as an active antidepressant based on a meta-analysis of trials of *Hypericum* in depression (published in the same issue). It was concluded that there was no doubt St John's wort was an effective antidepressant in mild to moderate cases but the number of properly controlled trials reported was limited. It had been widely assumed that hypericin was the active principle, but more evidence was required to prove this. The authors suggested that it was necessary to conduct (i) trials lasting longer than six weeks and (ii) other trials in severely depressed patients. They also recommended estimating the risk of relapse in patients who required long-term treatment. These other trials were carried out and St John's

When crushed the flowers of St John's wort produce an oil of a startling red colour, thought to represent the blood of St John the Baptist.

wort was found to have no effect in the treatment of severe depression. It was also noted that, in line with other antidepressants, hypericin has to be taken for two to four weeks before it begins to elevate the mood. However, the plant extract appears to be well tolerated, with few side-effects.

Evidence is now accumulating that would call into question whether hypericin is indeed the active principle of St John's wort. It is now suspected that hyperforin, another chemical component of this plant, may be the active principle and the results of a study of 147 patients with mild to moderate depression suggests that it is indeed hyperforin and not hypericin that is responsible for the antidepressant pharmacological activity of the plant. Scientists are still not entirely certain, however, whether the antidepressant effects are down to hypericin, hyperforin or a mixture of the two.

Evidence has emerged of certain dangers, direct and indirect, of St John's wort. It has been found that it interferes with the effect of certain common prescription drugs such as antibiotics, anticoagulants, painkillers and other antidepressants. In certain cases this chemical interaction may lead to fatal bleeding. Many regular users of St John's wort buy it over the counter; they neglect to mention this to their doctor as they see it as a mild herbal supplement and are unaware that it may be contra-indicated with prescription drugs.

Hypericin

Hypericum red

$C_{30}H_{16}O_8$

Hyperforin

$C_{35}H_{52}O_4$

We can, of course, never be certain as to how physicians and herbalists of ancient times recognised St John's wort as a remedy for both physical and mental ailments and can only presume that, as was usually the case, it was a matter of trial and error or plain chance. The infusion of the plant into oil produced a blood-coloured solution which by the doctrine of signatures suggested a use for bleeding wounds. Thus the armpit package of St Columba might have given rest and sleep to minds disordered by sepsis or fever. It would then be but a small step to its use for minds possessed by demons. At all events, the long story of St John's wort from pagan times through to the Christian medieval period is a fascinating one. St John's wort can now be said to justify its distinguished medieval title of the devil's scourge and enable us to drive out the melancholy demons of the 21st century.

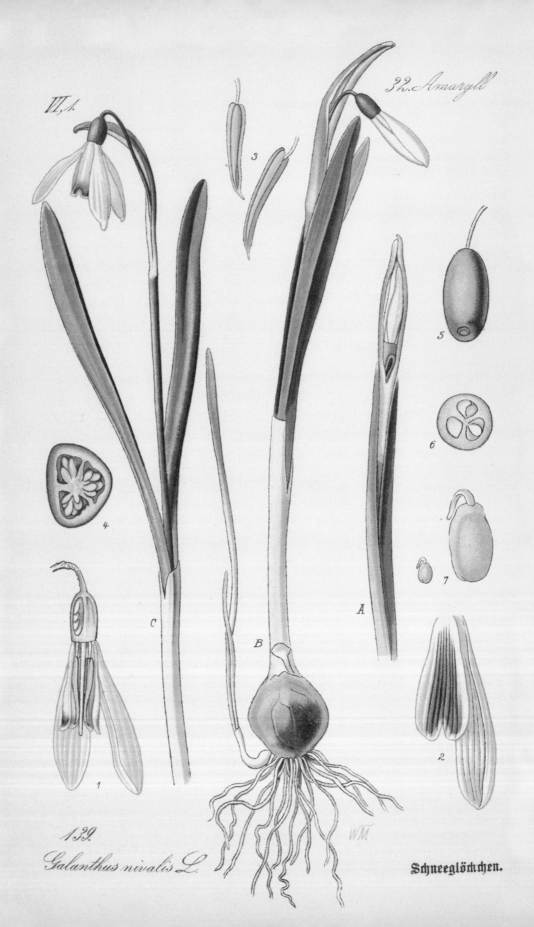

VII, 1.

32. Amaryll

139
Galanthus nivalis L.

Schneeglöckchen.

5 – The Snowdrop *(Galanthus nivalis)*: From Odysseus to Alzheimer

The author Robert Graves, in his work *The Greek Myths*, suggested that these ancient myths embodied folk memories of past events. One interesting example is the role that may have been played by the snowdrop (*Galanthus nivalis*) in Odysseus' encounter with the enchantress Circe, as recounted in Homer's *Odyssey*, which chimes with much of the knowledge we now have about the chemistry of the plant. It is thought that moly, the antidote to Circe's poison, may well have been an extract of snowdrop. The plant has also given us a modern-day drug, galantamine, a compound that has been used to help reduce some of the symptoms of Alzheimer's disease. This intriguing blend of ancient and modern uses is the reason for its inclusion in this book.

The generic name *Galanthus* comes from the Greek *gala* (milk) and *anthos* (flower) and refers to the milk-white petals. The genus belongs in the Amaryllidaceae family (along with garlic and daffodils) and comprises some 19 species of small perennial bulbous herbs. The leaves are linear (or elliptical) and the flowers solitary and nodding. Native to Europe and SW Asia, from the Pyrenees to the Caspian Sea, they were introduced into Britain in the early medieval period by religious communities and subsequently became widely naturalised. Notable colonies exist at many ancient monastic sites including Maltby in Yorkshire, Dunwich in Suffolk and Rothbury in Northumberland. One of the most northerly sites is an old graveyard outside Cromarty on the Black Isle. The plant appears to have escaped from these monastic colonies by direct transport of the bulbs or by being carried downstream in local flooding. The common snowdrop, *G. nivalis*, is native to central and eastern Europe, has narrow linear leaves and exists in many cultivars and varieties. The outer three petal-like tepals are long and conceal the inner three,

which are usually marked in green. In many parts of Europe snowdrops grow in damp deciduous woodland, often beside rivers and streams. They flower in late January to early February. For this reason they have been associated with Candlemas Day, the Christian holiday that falls on 2 February, and are often known as Candlemas bells. Other traditional names for them include

Medici/Mary Evans

The ruins of Walsingham Abbey with snowdrops growing in the foreground.

February fairmaids, dingle-dangle and snow-piercers (like the French *perce-neige*). Another species, *G. elwesii*, is named after the British naturalist Henry John Elwes (1846–1922) and a third, *G. fosteri*, after the distinguished physiologist Sir Michael Foster (1836–1907).

The History of the Snowdrop

The common name 'snowdrop' was first used in English by the botanist John Gerard (1545–1612), who described it in the 1633 edition of his *Herball*. The word seems not to be derived, as one might suppose, from the flower's resemblance to a drop of snow, nor from any association with its flowering

The frontispiece of John Gerard's celebrated *Herball* in which the name 'snowdrop' was first used.

when snow is 'dropping' to the ground, but rather from the drop earring. The most likely etymology is that it is a literal translation of the German *Schneetropf*, *Tropf* being the German word for that style of pendant-shaped earring popular at the time.

The flowers have various symbolic associations. They were brought into churches on Candlemas as a symbol of virginity and purity; village maidens would also wear them in garlands on this day. By contrast, the flowers were also regarded as a symbol of death because a single bloom was said to resemble a corpse with its head in a shroud. Consequently it was thought to be unlucky to bring a flower into the house. According to Christian legend, Eve wept with despair at her first sight of snow after leaving the Garden of Eden. An angel transformed the snowflakes into snowdrops to reassure her that spring was on its way. Similarly, Saint Francis of Assisi called the flower an emblem of hope, as it bloomed at the end of winter.

By the 16th and 17th centuries, the plant was commonly known. It was described by both the diarist and gardener John Evelyn (1620–1706) and the chemist Robert Boyle (1627–1691). The poet Thomas Tickell (1685–1740) referred to it as 'vegetable snow'[1] and in the 19th century the Poet Laureate Alfred, Lord Tennyson (1809–1892) mentioned it in the poem 'St Agnes' Eve'. On a more practical level, they were often planted in parallel lines to guide cottage dwellers to their outside privies on winter nights!

Homer's *Odyssey*

Odysseus, the mythical king of Ithaca who roamed the Aegean after the siege of Troy, as described by Homer in his epic poem *Odyssey*, arrived at the island of Aeaea on which the enchantress Circe lived. Circe gave food to the sailors in Odysseus' crew,

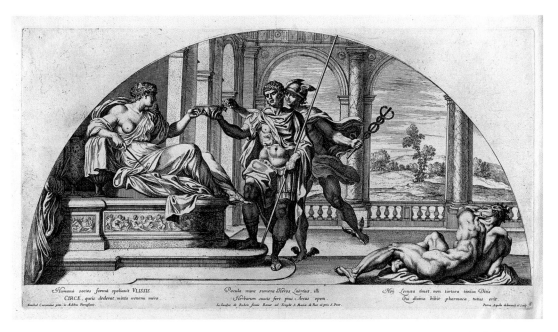

Circe with Odysseus and Hermes; the enchantress turned Odysseus' men into pigs by poisoning their food. The plant Hermes provided Odysseus with, very likely snowdrop from its description saved him from the same fate.

but, unhappily for them, the sorceress had mixed the food with a potion that turned the men into pigs. Odysseus set out to rescue his men. As he walked through the forest, he encountered the god Hermes in the form of a young man. Hermes warned him of the risk of meeting Circe and said that he would need to eat a magical herb called moly in order to protect himself from Circe's drug. He provided Odysseus with this antidote by 'pull[ing] the herb out of the ground … The root was black, while the flower was as white as milk.'[2] Circe tried to cast her spell on Odysseus but the moly ensured that he was able to resist her magical powers. Circe in turn was charmed by Odysseus' resistance and pleaded for mercy, saying, 'How can it be that my drugs have no power to charm you? Never yet was any man able to stand so much as a taste of the herb I gave you.'[3] She released his sailors and turned them back into men. They all remained on the island feasting for another year before their return to Ithaca.

Over the centuries two plants have emerged as likely candidates for Circe's poison from its description: it is thought to be either *Atropa*, from the family Solanaceae (see Chapter 1) or enchanter's nightshade (*Circaea lutetiana*), a member of the evening primrose family, Onagraceae. Just as intriguing, however, is the question of the antidote: what is the mythical herb moly and how could it antagonise a tropane alkaloid such as that found in *Atropa*? In 1983 a convincing argument was put forward that moly was in fact *Galanthus nivalis*, the common snowdrop.[4] First, Homer's description of where it was found, the colour of its flower and the black root fit the description of the snowdrop (or related *Galanthus* species) well. Second, galantamine, one of the chemicals in the bulb, would act as an anticholinesterase and reverse the actions of a tropane alkaloid such as hyoscine or atropine, so chemically it would work as an antidote.

Persuasive as this theory is, it is only one of a series of hypotheses that have been

The Greek botanist and physician Dioscorides suggested that the snowflake (*Leucojum vernum*) was a candidate for Hermes' antidote. The plant is in the same family as the snowdrop, Amaryllidaceae, and also contains galantamine.

Dioscorides.

posited over the centuries. Greek philosopher and botanist Theophrastus (c. 372–287 BC), in the third century BC, identified it as a variety of *Scilla*, a genus of perennial herbs from the family Asparagaceae. Much later, the English chemist John Goodyer (1592–1664) suggested that the plant was black garlic (*Allium nigrum*), an ornamental member of the onion family. Dioscorides (c. AD 40–90), the Greek botanist and physician, had earlier suggested the snowflake (*Leucojum vernum*); this is eminently possible as many members of the Amaryllidaceae contain the active principle galantamine. In any case, Homer's description of the effect of moly on Odysseus may be the first suggested example of the use of an anticholinesterase drug to prevent (or reverse) poisoning with a tropane alkaloid, such as atropine or hyoscine.

Work to extract and identify the active ingredient began in the 1950s and was carried out principally by Russian and Bulgarian pharmacologists. The structure of the active alkaloid of the family Amaryllidaceae was established as galantamine. This active principle occurs in several other genera of Amaryllidaceae: *Crinum*, *Hemerocallis*, *Hippeastrum*, *Leucojum*, *Lycoris*, *Narcissus* and *Ungeria* and consequently it has been known variously as galantamine, galanthine, lycorimine and lycorenine. It is often accompanied in these plants by the compound lycorine, which is more toxic and causes profuse vomiting. This latter compound may also account for the poisonous effect of the bulbs of narcissi such as daffodils. Galantamine was isolated from the Caucasian snowdrop (*Galanthus caucasicus*) in 1952 and from *Galanthus nivalis* in 1954. As most of the original work on galantamine was carried out in Eastern Bloc countries between 1950 and 1960, it took some time before the results filtered through to the West and attracted any attention there.

An illustrated text from around 1420 showing Odysseus brandishing the flowers as he approaches Circe, followed by his men who have been turned into various beasts.

Galantamine

Galantamine inhibits acetylcholinesterase in all tissues. As a result of this, it was used for some years to reverse muscle relaxants such as tubocurarine, used in anaesthesia (see Chapter 7). Reports of this, however, were anecdotal and difficult to evaluate until 1971, when the Finnish physician Dimitri Cozanitis reported on 40 patients undergoing surgery. Using intravenous doses of galantamine ranging from 5 mg to 20 mg he was able to reverse the effect of tubocurarine. The rate of recovery of muscular activity was slower than with neostigmine, an alternative drug derived from physostigmine. The side-effects of galantamine included nausea, vomiting, salivation and blurred vision. In tests on rabbits, galantamine eye drops lowered the pressure of the fluid inside the eye, and the duration of this effect was much longer than that seen with the drug physostigmine, a commonly used

Galantamine

$$C_{17}H_{21}NO_3$$

drug at the time. The compound therefore had the potential to be of use as a treatment for glaucoma, although it has subsequently been replaced by more effective drugs. Galantamine also had positive effects on memory in rats in various experimental models, which led to its evaluation as a potential therapy in Alzheimer's disease.

Galantamine and Alzheimer's Disease

Alois Alzheimer (1864–1915) was a leading German neuropathologist and psychiatrist, an expert on diseases of the nervous system. Together with his lifelong friend and collaborator Franz Nissl (1860–1919) he published a six-volume treatise entitled *Histologic and Histopathologic Studies of the Cerebral Cortex*. His marriage to the rich widow of a banker meant he was in the happy position of being able to fund his own research, in particular the expensive

The German neuropathologist and psychiatrist Alois Alzheimer. His investigations into a disorder of the cerebral cortex led to the disease bearing his name. Galantamine was thought to possess several features which would have a positive effect on the brains of sufferers.

Science Photo Library

illustrations of neuropathology specimens in his papers and books. A devoted teacher, he was also known for his pince-nez and ever-present cigar.

In 1906 Alzheimer described the clinical and neuropathological features of a woman aged 51 who had died after a progressive illness that had lasted for five years and had been characterised by depression and hallucinations. Progressive dementia then ensued. A post mortem revealed wasting of the brain tissue. Silver staining, a method of detecting trace amounts of protein, showed neurofibrillary tangles, a build-up of the protein tau forming tangles in the nerve cells, and senile plaques, small deposits of the amyloid-beta protein that form outside the brain cells. These have been recognised as the pathological hallmarks for the disease which now bears Alzheimer's name. Now, over 100 years later, we know that the disease is characterised by the widespread deposition of amyloid in the brain, accompanied by a serious reduction in brain transmitters and in particular a marked fall in the concentration of acetylcholine in the cerebral cortex.

A computer processed image of a vertical slice through the brain of an Alzheimer's patient on the left, and a comparatively healthy brain on the right. The brain with Alzheimer's disease is shrunken due to the degeneration and death of nerve cells.

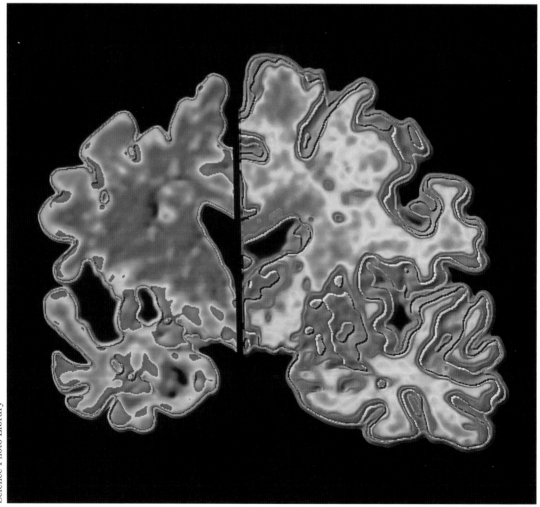

As a result of similarities between Alzheimer's disease and Parkinson's disease, methods used in the treatment of the latter were considered for Alzheimer's disease in the 1980s. These focused on the effects of action on the cholinergic system in an attempt to increase its activity. It was realised from the outset that not all Alzheimer's sufferers would benefit, because the condition varies widely both clinically and genetically. The most common strategy adopted was to attempt to inhibit the destructive enzyme acetylcholinesterase in the brain. The classic drug physostigmine was tried initially but was too toxic and too short-acting.

Galantamine was thought to possess several positive features as a treatment for Alzheimer's disease. It had been used in anaesthetic practice for a number of years and had proved reasonably safe. Moreover, the use of galantamine makes it fairly easy to achieve a substantial inhibition of cholinesterase in the brain, and it appears to be free of toxic effects on the liver. Pilot studies on its use in dementia were carried out in Vienna and Berlin and published in 1989. In a relatively small number of patients there appeared to be a positive effect and this encouraged randomised trials with a greater number of patients, which again had a positive effect on most patients. Some patients who received galantamine for periods of up to three years showed a lower rate of cognitive decline when compared with the control group. The side-effects were dose-dependent, mild and tended to disappear with prolonged treatment. There were no harmful effects on liver or kidney function. It appeared that galantamine compared favourably with other drugs in the anticholinesterase category. Although more recent information has shown that none of these drugs appears to actually extend the lifespan of Alzheimer's patients, they all nevertheless have a useful palliative effect and keep patients in the community for a longer period, reducing the demand for expensive and prolonged institutional care.

> Deep on the convent-roof the snows
> Are sparkling to the moon:
> My breath to heaven like vapour goes;
> May my soul follow soon!
> The shadows of the convent-towers
> Slant down the snowy sward,
> Still creeping with the creeping hours
> That lead me to my Lord:
> Make Thou my spirit pure and clear
> As are the frosty skies,
> Or this first snowdrop of the year
> That in my bosom lies.
>
> Alfred, Lord Tennyson, *St Agnes Eve*

The galantamine story represents an end to an odyssey that stretches from Homer and the Greek gods to modern chemistry and neuropathology. The story is an interesting example of ancient wisdom linked to modern knowledge and well exemplifies Graves' views of the importance of the myth to ancient peoples. The antidote moly counteracted the mental effects of poison on Odysseus' men just as galantamine has been shown to act in positive ways on the brains of some Alzheimer's sufferers. Truly we can agree with the view expressed by Thomas Carlyle in his 1838 essay 'On History' when he wrote, 'What is all Knowledge too but recorded Experience and a product of History'. The snowdrop exemplifies this transmission from myth to plant, and onwards to medication and therapy.

B.D. Inglis

PLANTS OF THE BIBLE _ MANDRAGORA OFFICINARUM LINN. — MANDRAKE   PLATE 49

6 – The Mandrake (*Mandragora officinalis*): In League with the Devil

Of all the members of the Solanaceae family, the mandrake has perhaps the most curious history. The plant's somewhat unusual name probably derives from the Middle English or Middle Dutch *mandrage* (man + dragon), an allusion to its supposed magical powers. Shakespeare referred to 'mandragora' in both *Othello* and *Antony and Cleopatra*, and to the mandrake in *Henry VI* and *Romeo and Juliet*. In Act IV of the latter he mentions the shrieking of the mandrake when it is uprooted from the ground and that 'loving mortals hearing them run mad'.[1] The story of the mandrake is a long and turbulent one, and serves as a good example of the exaggerated claims of folklore sometimes holding a grain of scientific truth.

The mandrake is a low-growing perennial herb native to the Southern Mediterranean. Like *Atropa* and *Hyoscyamus*, which appear earlier in this book (in Chapters 1 and 3 respectively), and the potato, tomato and tobacco, it is a member of the family Solanaceae. It has a large taproot, a rosette of simple, very puckered leaves and solitary five-lobed bell-shaped flowers. Its fruits are yellow, aromatic and poisonous. They are sometimes known as devil's apples. At night, it is claimed, the plant exudes an unearthly light; Arabic tradition held that this was because it was possessed by a *djinn* (a spiritual creature who could be both benevolent and malevolent) which would guard the plant day and night. This fanciful idea led people to adopt curious methods of unearthing the plant, as will be seen later in the chapter.

The Mandrake in History and Legend

The mandrake is mentioned as far back as in Genesis, the first book of the Old Testament.[2] The story recounts how the boy Reuben goes into the fields and gathers a plant with yellow berries. He takes some of these berries back to his mother Leah. Leah's sister Rachel recognises the fruit as that of the mandrake and requests some for herself, as she is barren and wishes to use the plant to overcome the stigma of childlessness. Rachel later gives birth to Joseph, who goes on to play an illustrious part in Jewish history. In the Biblical context, the emphasis was on the power of the plant as an aid to fertility, with no mention of its narcotic properties.

Rachel and Leah at the well of Haran. In Genesis Rachel uses the yellow berries of the mandrake to cure her childlessness.

The Greek goddess of love, Aphrodite, also known as Mandragoritis. Her association with the plant is thought to be due to its supposed aphrodisiac properties.

The Greeks, on the other hand, were interested in different properties of the mandrake. They knew it to be a narcotic. Hippocrates (460–370 BC), considered the father of medicine, asserted in around 400 BC that a small dose in wine would relieve depression and anxiety, while Aristotle (384–322 BC) described the plant as a valuable soporific. Theophrastus (371–287 BC) wrote the first Greek treatise on plants in around 230 BC, in which he recommended the mandrake as a sovereign remedy for gout, sleeplessness and as a love potion. The Greeks also associated the plant with Aphrodite, the goddess of love, who was known as Mandragoritis, or 'she of the mandrake', a nod to the plant's supposed aphrodisiac properties.

> The phantom shapes – oh touch not them –
> That appals the murderer's sight,
> Lurk in the fleshy mandrake's stem,
> That shrieks when pluck'd at night!'
>
> Thomas Moore, *Lalla Rookh*

Theophrastus also refers to the fact that the taproot of the plant resembles a diminutive man, and it was from such early observations that the bizarre rites and ceremonies surrounding the plant were to emerge in the centuries that followed. His treatise contains the first clear description of the procedure that must be followed by the plant gatherer in order that he should not be bewitched by the mandrake. He should draw three circles around the plant with his sword. Then, facing the west to avoid evil spells, he should slice portions of the taproot. At the cutting of the second piece, he must dance around the plant and mutter incantations concerning the mystery of love. The drawing of three circles protects the gatherer from the plant and the sword used should be a magic one made of virgin iron and used exclusively for the purpose of mandrake gathering.

The next important Greek authority to pay particular attention to the mandrake was the Greek physician Dioscorides (c. AD 40–90), who had recorded the results of his investigations into the world of plants in a manuscript entitled *De Materia Medica*, a copy of which was made for a Byzantine princess and named the *Juliana Anicia Codex* after her. In the book are two full-page miniatures devoted to the mandrake. In the first, Euresis, the goddess of discovery, offers Dioscorides a specimen of the mandrake root. Also seen in the picture is a dog that has succumbed to the evil effects of the plant. In the second miniature, Dioscorides is shown drawing the root of the mandrake. He mentions a number of the other names that have been used for the herb but suggests firmly that *Mandragora* should be adopted.

He also notes that there are 'male' and 'female' forms and confirms the views of Theophrastus that the root and fruit are useful for a variety of illnesses and perhaps as a love potion or fertility drug.

From 500 BC onwards, physicians and philosophers migrated from Greece to Rome and took with them the knowledge that they had acquired from the early disciples of Asklepios, the god of healing, among whom were Theophrastus and Dioscorides. The first Roman author to investigate the mandrake appears to have been Pliny the Elder (AD 23–79). He commended it for all the ailments cited above, adding that it was also useful for soothing inflammation of the eyes. He also concluded that there were two varieties of the mandrake, *vernalis* (flowering in the spring) and *autumnalis* (flowering in the autumn), although modern studies show no evidence of this.

Dioscorides Describing the Mandrake, a 1909 painting by Ernest Board.

The Romans also believed that the plant might be used for military as well as medicinal purposes. Two stories circulated widely amongst the Roman high command. The first related to the Carthaginian general Hannibal (247–182 BC) who, when his army was fighting African rebels, pretended to retreat. He then left behind on the battlefield a number of jars of wine which had been fortified with mandrake. The rebels drank the wine and fell into a stupor, thus allowing Hannibal and his men to return and kill them all. Another anecdote is recounted regarding Julius Caesar, who was captured by pirates and employed a similar stratagem to gain his release.

A manikin, the shape of the roots resembling a kneeling man screaming. These were much sought after, passed through families as heirlooms, and were believed to bring good luck.

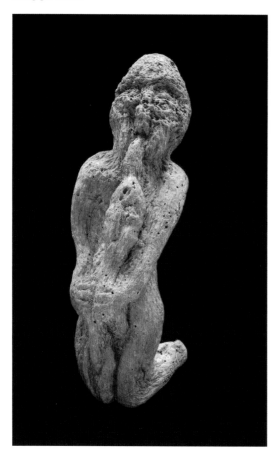

After the fall of the Roman Empire little was heard of the mandrake in Europe until the Anglo-Saxon period. The late 15th century saw the first publication of *Herbarium Apuleii Platonici*, or *Herbarium of Apuleius*, thought to have been written in the 4th or 5th century and usually attributed to the writer Pseudo-Apuleius. In this volume the mandrake is described as beneficial for all sorts of ailments. The author noted that at night the leaves shine brightly, like a lamp, thought to be a sign of supernatural possession. He also modified the Greeks' instructions with regard to harvesting in two important ways. First, instead of a man digging up the roots himself, a dog should be used to jerk them from the ground. Second, an ivory staff should be used to loosen them, as ivory was thought to be a talisman against evil. It was then advised that, similar to the Greek method, an iron sword should then be used to cut the roots into manageable portions. The reasoning behind this detailed procedure was that the gatherer of the plant should do his utmost to avoid being contaminated by the malign spirit that supposedly lived in the plant. However, if the plant was pulled from the ground on holy days, the spirit would appear to the gatherer and do his bidding, reminiscent of the *djinn* of Arabic tradition, who could be a force for both good and evil.

A dried mandrake root in the home was thought to bring good luck and prosperity and to protect the household from evil spirits. The mandrake is not indigenous to Britain, however, and consequently its dried roots had to be imported, often at great expense. The dried root in its native form (or as a carved manikin or homunculus) became a prized family heirloom and was often bequeathed specifically in wills. As a result of its rarity and value, a search was made for native plants that could act as a poor man's substitute. The plants that medieval herbalists came up with were the black briony (*Dioscorea communis*) and white briony (*Bryonia cretica* subsp. *dioica*), from the families Dioscoreaceae and Cucurbitaceae respectively. The roots of both plants resemble those of the mandrake; they can be carved into shapes and contain similar narcotic poisons. From the 13th to 16th centuries there was considerable trade in Britain and Europe in these and other convincing substitutes for the mandrake.

The Sceptical Herbalists, 1500 to 1800

The 16th and 17th centuries saw the advent of the era of rationalism, in which traditional herbalism was called into question and many superstitions were jettisoned. The power of the mandrake root to protect against ill fortune and the rituals surrounding its gathering were consigned to history, although its therapeutic use continued. One of the most interesting early accounts in this period is that by William Turner (c. 1508–1568), a physician and naturalist whose *Herbal* was printed in 1551. In it, he describes the male and female forms of the root. If the root had divided into two, it was considered to be male, as it looked as though it had legs. These male forms were called manikins. The female forms, known as puppettes, had not divided in this way and were thought to resemble a female body. Turner condemned the fact that manikins and puppettes were carved from the plants and sold to the gullible.

A further important account was that of the botanist and herbalist John Gerard (1545–1612) in his *Herball* of 1597, in which he too castigates the prevalent folk tales as being propagated by 'old wives, runagate surgeons or physickmongers' and accused 'idle

Three people plucking the mandrake from the ground with long strings.

drones' of carving manikins from these plants and then passing them off to the superstitious as the true mandrake.[3] John Parkinson (1567–1650), herbalist by Royal Appointment to the Court of Charles I, was another influential authority to rail against the mandrake. In *A Garden of Pleasant Flowers* (1629), he blames the chief magistrates of the City of London for tolerating the sale of mandrake manikins, urging them to prosecute the vendors of such 'toys which are ridiculous products of man's invention'.[4]

These herbalists, while dismissing the harvesting rites and manikins as superstitious nonsense, nonetheless accepted that the mandrake had properties that meant it could be used as a soporific, painkiller and mild local anaesthetic. It might also be used externally to treat such conditions as eye infections and scrofulous tumours. Moreover, it was thought that any undesirable effects, such as torpor, confusion and coma, could be reversed by wormwood, rue, marjoram or castor oil.

Benjamin Ward Richardson, the physician and anaesthetist who carried out experiments on the effects of mandrake in the 1880s.

Mandrake and the History of Anaesthesia

The soporific and anaesthetic properties of the mandrake were described by the classical authors, such as Socrates, Theophrastus and Dioscorides, over many centuries. In particular, Dioscorides outlined the process by which strips of mandrake bark were steeped in sweet wine for months. This wine contained the narcotic principle and became known in Roman times as the 'death wine' or 'morion'. It was given to the victims of torture or crucifixion. Sometimes another bitter anaesthetic, such as myrrh (*Commiphora myrrha*), was added to the mandrake to potentiate its effects. Thus it follows that the next important step in the development of mandrake as an anaesthetic was that of the soporific sponge (see Chapter 3).

Several centuries later, in 1888, Benjamin Ward Richardson (1828–1896), a physician and anaesthetist, began a series of investigations into the mandrake. He procured a supply of the *Mandragora* root from Greece and, following the ancient recipe of Dioscorides, made a tincture in an alcohol/water mixture, steeping the root for a period of four weeks. He found that this tincture would sedate and anaesthetise animals, particularly cats and dogs. He also noted that the animal's pupils dilated and concluded that the extract must contain one or more alkaloids similar to hyoscine or atropine (most probably the former). In the course of his experiments on different animals, he also found, to his surprise, that pigeons were much more sensitive to this infusion than rabbits. We know now that the rabbit gut and liver contain an enzyme called atropinase which can destroy solanaceous alkaloids and allows the animal to feed on nightshade (*Atropa*) and henbane (*Hyoscyamus*). Presumably they could also consume the mandrake with relative impunity.

Finally, Richardson tried small doses of the mandrake infusion on himself and noted that he experienced numbness of the

A label for mandrake pills.

tongue, dryness of the mouth, confused vision, restlessness and exaggerated sensitivity to sounds. On the basis of these findings he concluded that if the alkaloid could be identified and extracted it might be used as an anaesthetic or possibly supersede atropine as a dilator of the pupil. He also foresaw its use as a treatment for strychnine poisoning and tetanus. Richardson's work was the first to apply modern scientific procedures to the mandrake and at the time aroused a great deal of interest. In 1889, Felix B. Ahrens (1863–1910), a German professor and chemist, isolated an alkaloid from *Mandragora* which he called 'mandragorine'. However, in the early 1900s it was discovered that Ahrens' compound was in fact a mixture of hyoscyamine, hyoscine and a small amount of a third alkaloid for which the name mandragorine was retained. Despite this flurry of interest in the chemical constituents of mandrake, it was too late for the development of the plant as an anaesthetic.

The history of the mandrake, as we have seen, is an intriguing one. A plant that could produce a deep sleep and which also glowed in the dark was obviously a very special one. As madness in the Christian tradition was often ascribed to the possession of the mind by an evil spirit, so the mandrake was the 'home' of a similar malevolent being. Moreover, the power of the myth was strengthened by the fact that the roots, either naturally or after carving, closely resembled the shape of a man's body. The scene was thus set for an illiterate credulous people to invest the mandrake with all sorts of magical powers and to develop complex rituals in order to harvest it without harming themselves or interfering with its potency. The situation changed materially with the arrival of the modern herbalists who poured scorn on the old beliefs. Finally, the advent of more effective and less dangerous anaesthetic compounds such as nitrous oxide, ether and chloroform put paid, once and for all, to its use in anaesthesia.

7 – Curare (*Chondrodendron tomentosum*): A South American Arrow Poison

As the Conquistadors were penetrating South America in the 16th century, anecdotes from their travels filtered back to Europe, including tales of how the natives were using arrows tipped by a deadly poison, often delivered by a blowpipe. It was said that men and horses were killed and their deaths preceded by a profound and terrifying state of paralysis. Many different explorers tried, without success, to identify the poison. Eventually it was established that the toxin was derived from plants. The main plant used as a source for this deadly arrow poison was identified as the liana *Chondrodendron tomentosum*; from it, the pure alkaloid d-tubocurarine was finally isolated. This alkaloid was the first effective muscle relaxant, representing a major advance in surgical anaesthesia and electroconvulsive therapy.

*C*hondrodendron tomentosum is a climbing plant, a member of the family Menispermaceae. It was first described fully in 1794 by the Spanish botanists Hipólito Ruiz López (1754–1816) and José Antonio Pavón Jiménez (1754–1840), in their *Flora of Peru*. Local names for the plant include *Pareira brava* (literally 'wild vine'). The generic name is derived from the Greek *chondros* (meaning 'granule') and *dendros* ('tree'). This name refers to the warty protrusions on the bark. The stem of this climber can exceed 10 cm in diameter. The leaves alternate up the stem and are covered with a short, dense down on the underside. It is dioecious, with separate male and female plants. Male flowers have six sepals, six petals and six stamens while the female flowers have six carpels each with a single ovule inside. The fruit is a drupe, purplish-black in colour and around 2 cm in length. When these become fully ripe they look similar to a bunch of grapes. The roots are long and extremely bitter to taste, no doubt due to the bitter alkaloid. Originally the root was used to treat inflammation of the bladder and the kidney, and to dissolve urinary stones. As a cure for these disorders it proved spurious, as was the Brazilian belief that the root could cure the bites of venomous serpents.

Chondrodendron and Curare

Charles Waterton (1782–1865), a naturalist and explorer from Yorkshire, made several exploratory trips to South America. He discovered that the Macushi tribe used an arrow poison which seemed to act far more quickly than *Strychnos*, previously supposed to be the main constituent of all South American arrow poisons. Different tribes called Waterton's new discovery by various names, with the English name curare derived from the Carib word *wurari*. Curare was originally classified into three types,

South American Indians preparing curare, a highly complex ritual.

"It was the first and last time I was ever on a Cayman's back."
vide "Wanderings in South America" by
Charles Waterton Esq." page 232."

dependent on the container it was packed and transported in: tube curare, pot curare and calabash curare. It was discovered to be a complex mixture of components but derived mainly from one plant, and explorers soon realised that the plant had already been classified as *Chondrodendron tomentosum*

Small curare pots; the names of the vessels in which the poison was carried gave rise to its different names: pot curare, tube curare and calabash curare.

A coloured etching from 1827 showing Charles Waterton wrestling a cayman. The explorer and naturalist is thought to have been the first westerner to discover curare.

by Ruiz and Pavón. Pot curare often also contained *Strychnos* and crushed venomous ants, extracts of poisonous snakes were often added to all three types. There are, we now know, at least 25 species of *Chondrodendron* but only *C. tomentosum* contains appreciable concentrations of the alkaloid d-tubocurarine.

Strychnos and Strychnine

The term curare refers to the toxic extracts which make up the South American arrow poisons, the active component of which was initially believed to be *Strychnos*. In 1800, Alexander von Humboldt (1769–1859) witnessed the preparation of the arrow poison during an expedition to South America and he positively identified the active ingredient as a variety of *Strychnos*, another poisonous rainforest liana. The genus is widely distributed in Asia, Africa and South America where the common *S. toxifera* is used on arrows to paralyse prey of small mammals and birds.

In Asia the two most common species are *S. nux-vomica* and *S. Ignatii* (literally the vomiting nut and St Ignatius bean

Strychnine

$C_{21}H_{22}N_2O_2$

respectively). In this area they were both widely used as rodenticides. The seeds of *S. nux-vomica* contain about 1–3 per cent total alkaloids. These alkaloids are extremely toxic. The plant and seeds of *S. nux-vomica* were first introduced into the United Kingdom in 1778 and were principally used to kill rodents. In Germany the seeds were used to kill crows and hence were called *Krähenaugen* (crow's eyes).

At one time strychnine, first isolated in 1807, was used as a tonic for humans, in preparations such as Metatone and Easton's syrup, but these were abandoned as they were extremely dangerous. Strychnine can cause violent epileptic convulsions and severe contraction of the respiratory muscles, resulting in death from lack of oxygen. It is still used illegally in the United Kingdom to poison birds of prey. Ironically d-tubocurarine, the alkaloid obtained from its sister ingredient *C. tomentosum*, can be used as an antidote to strychnine poisoning.

Strychnos Nux Vomica

An 1889 painting of Claude Bernard with a group of pupils; Bernard discovered, through experimentation, that curare acted on the junction between muscle and nerve.

The 19th century saw scientists conduct several important experiments with curare. The physician Sir Benjamin Brodie (1783–1862) was the first to discover, in 1812, that curare poisoning does not stop the heart from beating, and showed that an animal kept alive through artifical respiration could make a full recovery. Charles Waterton, too, on his return from South America, conducted in 1825 a now famous experiment on a donkey, in which the animal was injected with curare but kept alive using a pair of bellows that artifically inflated its lungs through an incision in its windpipe. After several hours, the effects of the poison wore off and the animal apparently went on to live for another 20 years. In the 1850s the French physiologist Claude Bernard (1813–1878) obtained several samples of tube curare and carried out a series of experiments on the action of curare on a nerve and its muscle, in particular the sciatic nerve of the leg on the gastrocnemius muscle of the calf in the dog and the frog. He found that curare did not poison the sciatic nerve, nor did it poison the muscle itself. He suggested that it acted on the junction between the two, known as the neuromuscular junction. With the limited methods available at the time, however, he was unable to establish what exactly was happening at this junction. Later, in 1941, Richard Evans Schultes (1915–2001), an American ethnobotanist, received a grant to visit the Amazon region and conduct research into the arrow poisons used by the indigenous peoples, and in particular to find out which plants were used to make curare.

The Therapeutic Uses of D-tubocurarine

The alkaloid was discovered over time to have several therapeutic uses. The first was in electroconvulsive therapy (ECT) as a pre-medication. The production of fits by drugs or electrical shock had been developed in the 1930s to treat severe mental illness such as extreme depression and schizophrenia. The treatment was largely successful in the former, although of marginal benefit in the latter. In its original somewhat barbaric form, the violent convulsions often resulted in bone fractures, particularly in the hip and the spinal column. The pure extract of *Chondrodendron tomentosum*, when given to the patient after the general anaesthetic, acted as a muscle relaxant and as a result the incidence of major bone fracture was dramatically reduced.

The safety of surgical anaesthesia improved markedly with the advent of inhaled cyclopropane in the 1930s. This volatile gas replaced ether (which carried a danger of fire) and choloroform (which was toxic to the heart). One serious problem remained, however. The contraction of the abdominal

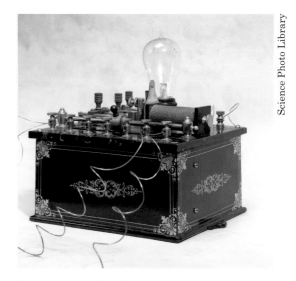

Science Photo Library

An apparatus used in electroconvulsive therapy. This controversial psychiatric treatment uses an electric current to induce a generalised seizure in patients suffering from severe mental disorders. Curare was used as a pre-medication to relax the muscles preventing bone fracture during the procedure.

muscles during anaesthesia made surgical access to the stomach, gut, gall bladder and spleen extremely difficult. What was needed was a muscle relaxant that could be given to patients before surgery. Pure d-tubocurarine was successfully tested on a sample of 25

An illustration of a man in a convulsion. This kind of spasm is a common symptom of both tetanus and strychnine poisoning.

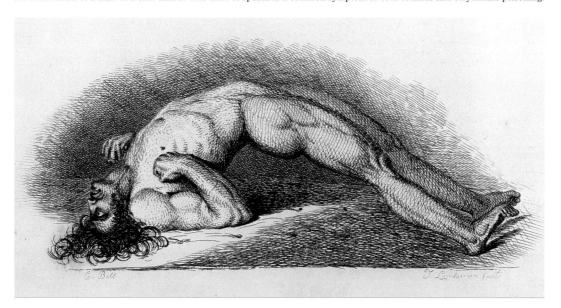

patients to relax their abdominal muscles. As a result of the successful outcome of this trial, the number of surgical patients subsequently given d-tubocurarine as a muscle relaxant then increased quite significantly. If recovery of the muscle tone was delayed for any reason, then physostigmine or a related drug could be administered, which would rapidly reverse the effect of the anticholinergic d-tubocurarine.

In the developed world tetanus and strychnine poisoning have virtually disappeared, but in developing countries they are still a widespread problem. Tetanus is caused by a toxin produced by the bacterium *Clostridium tetani*, often present in soil and animal manure, which can infect open wounds. Its bacterial toxin paralyses the respiratory muscles and the patient dies of lack of oxygen. Strychnine poisoning produces similar spasms and the two conditions can often be confused. In 1850, the Scottish physician George Harley (1829–1896) showed that curare was an effective treatment for strychnine poisoning. Both conditions have a very high mortality rate (greater than 90 per cent) but the use of curare as a muscle relaxant has reduced this in both conditions to less than 10 per cent.

This chapter has described an epic journey from the dark rainforests of South America to the operating theatres of the world; from an impure native arrow poison to the pure crystalline alkaloid d-tubocurarine. The latter, as the first effective muscle relaxant, proved to be a landmark drug in the field of anaesthetics. This substance, and its modern congeners, have made abdominal surgery easier, safer and much more successful. The journey has been a long and arduous one, with many obstacles to circumvent.

Kill the Prime Minister

Political assassination in the UK is a rare occurrence indeed. The most notable examples were in 1628 when the Duke of Buckingham was killed by a disaffected soldier and then in 1812, when Prime Minister Spencer Perceval was killed by John Bellingham in the House of Commons, the first and only British Prime Minister ever to be assassinated. During the First World War, however, a bizarre plot emerged to kill both the Prime Minister, David Lloyd George, and the Paymaster-General, Arthur Henderson. The plot revolved around a Mrs Alice Wheeldon, her two daughters and her son-in-law, Alfred Mason, who owned a chemist's shop in Southampton. One daughter lived with Mrs Wheeldon in Derby and acted as a go-between, while the other was married to Mason. These supposed plotters were socialists and conscientious objectors, disgruntled with the war and annoyed with the political system as a whole. Their group was, however, infiltrated by one 'Alex Gordon', who reported that they were hatching a plot to murder the two prominent politicians.

Gordon informed the British Head of Intelligence, Major Melville Lee, who promptly sent a second agent, Herbert Booth, to Derby in the hope of gaining further information. Booth was also able to infiltrate the group and they apparently gave him an airgun together with pellets and darts that had been dipped in curare. Armed with this potentially lethal weapon, he was

An image from *The Illustrated London News* of February 1917 showing Alice Wheeldon and her daughters in H.M. Prison Holloway.

allegedly instructed to hide on Walton Heath Golf Course in Surrey, and to ambush and shoot the Prime Minister. Mr Mason also sent a parcel to Herbert Booth in Derby which contained two tubes of strychnine and two of curare. All this material was handed over by the Secret Service to Bernard Spilsbury, the famous pathologist. He identified both poisons and gave his opinion that there was enough curare to kill several people.

As a result of all the evidence, the four conspirators were arrested and brought to trial. Their defence was that they intended to use the curare to kill, or disable, guard dogs. The Attorney General disposed of this argument with relish and the jury decided that three of the accused were guilty.

Mrs Wheeldon received a sentence of ten years, Mr Mason, seven, and Mrs Mason, five. Mrs Wheeldon's other daughter was acquitted. Was the plot feasible? Perhaps. However strychnine would seem in some way a more powerful threat than curare if Lloyd George's domestic servants could have been corrupted. Certainly the chances of hitting Lloyd George with a poison dart would seem somewhat slim, whether at Walton Heath or anywhere else. It is worth noting that many authorities now believe much of the evidence against Wheeldon was fabricated. Lloyd George released her after she had served only nine months of her sentence and she died only a short time later in the Spanish flu epidemic.

Illustrated London News Ltd./Mary Evans

Tab. 121.

SOLANUM TUBEROSUM L.
Die Erdæpfel.

8 – The Potato (*Solanum tuberosum*):
From the Andes to Europe

Whether seen in gardens or supermarkets, the potato is a familiar crop to most of us. It is probable that the modern potato (*Solanum tuberosum*) originated in the South American *altiplano* – the high plains of the Andes – about 13,000 years ago. The tuber itself appears to have been first cultivated by the Andeans between 7,000 and 10,000 years ago in an area that is now part of southern Peru and north-western Bolivia. It became a staple crop because it grew in conditions where cereals could not survive and could also be stored for lengthy periods of time. The Andeans worked on the plants for centuries, developing hardier varieties. The potato is now fourth in terms of tonnage in the world league table of crops (after rice, wheat and maize).

The potato is a robust, usually hairless perennial herb that dies back each year to the tubers. With over 1,200 species, *Solanum* is the largest genus in Solanaceae – a family famed for its alkaloids, and one which appears throughout this book. The characteristic lilac flowers are the typical

The English herbalist John Gerard as pictured on the frontispiece of his 1597 *Herball*. In his hand he is holding flowers from the potato plant.

Science Photo Library

form in the genus, with bunched anthers shaking pollen onto visiting bees like a pepper pot. When a cultivated potato is compared with one of its wild ancestors, two important differences are noticeable. First, the cultivated variety weighs around twice as much and second, it tastes much less bitter than its wild counterpart. Each potato flower can readily crossbreed with its neighbours. If the plant is allowed to flower, around 200 seeds per flower are produced and the opportunity of new cultivars is enhanced. The Andeans, by crossbreeding the flowers, managed to produce a number of varieties, as have modern-day growers. Around 5,000 varieties are now grown worldwide.

The History of the Potato

When the Spanish Conquistadors arrived in the altiplano in the early 16th century, they were predominantly searching for silver and gold, but as they developed the mining and smelting industries they also studied native customs and became aware of plants including the potato, *Cinchona* and *Erythroxylum coca*, all of which they came to realise were valuable.

The potato went on to become a staple food crop in South America for several reasons. First, it could survive the wild swings of temperature on the altiplano, as well as the

A 1757 line engraving of Sir Walter Raleigh whose name is often associated with the history of the potato's journey to Europe. It is now widely accepted that it is unlikely he was responsible for this development.

by accident in someone's baggage and was initially regarded as of little importance. Indeed, the Spanish saw the potato as an inferior food fit only for the poor or for pigs. Up to the year 1600, *Solanum tuberosum* was grown only by botanists in royal and academic gardens. Attempts were made to persuade the local peasants in Spain and France to start growing the potato but they resisted stoutly; they were used to dealing with plants that had seeds and using these to sow the next season's crop, while the potato was propagated by peculiar excrescences.

In Britain there was a traditional reliance on cereal crops such as wheat, barley and oats, and up until the 18th century potatoes were mostly fed to cattle and pigs. However, the population of England began to increase sharply around this time, and extra food was required. Further, the cost of bread swallowed up most of the money that labourers had to spend on sustenance. As a result potatoes began to be cultivated for human consumption in the north-west of England where the weather was on the whole mild and wet. Small parcels of land were often given to the agricultural labourer or rented cheaply by the factory worker. The potato increasingly replaced bread as the staple foodstuff. As the canal system expanded in the late 1700s, it became possible to ship potatoes between Liverpool, Manchester and Birmingham.

A serious setback occurred in the 1770s. The Lancashire potato fields were stricken by the disease *Verticillium atroalbum*, commonly known as 'leaf curl'. This potentially serious disease, which causes the leaves of the plant to become deformed and the potato to wilt and die, is transmitted by aphids. The Lancashire crop failed and extreme hunger resulted in some areas in the North. By the early 19th century only a few areas of Britain were heavily

prolonged periods of drought that render cereals such as wheat, corn and barley unviable. Most of the rural vegetation is dwarf and scrublike. The potato not only survives but thrives at altitudes of up to 5,000 m. The starch present in high concentration in its tubers will support the plant through drought and other extremes of weather for months at a time. Second, the tuber could also be easily stored. Keeping food on the altiplano was difficult but the Andeans circumvented the problem of storage by developing a freeze-dried preparation of potato called *chuño*, made by letting part of the tuber harvest freeze overnight and then squeezing some of the water from the flesh. Chuño could remain edible for up to ten years when stored in a sealed room and could be rapidly reconstituted by heating in boiling water. Third, given the scarcity of fuel, cooking was not always easy. The potato could be cooked on an open fire without the need for complex cooking equipment. Finally, the Andeans also came to realise that the potato had a yield that far exceeded that produced by cereal crops.

How the potato was transported to Europe is something of a mystery but it seems to have arrived in Spain in around 1570, some 50 years after the colonists had discovered it in South America. It was probably transported

Ireland and the Potato Famine

Any history of the potato is bound up irrevocably with the story of the Irish famine, one of the great tragedies of the 19th century.

The commonly accepted story is that the potato was introduced to Ireland by Sir Walter Raleigh to his estates near Youghal in County Cork. Like so many stories about Raleigh, there is no definite evidence for this notion. It is more likely that it was taken to County Wicklow by English emigrants who fled the English Civil War in the 1640s and settled there before moving out to the west of the country. The potato was extremely well adapted to the Irish climate for several reasons. Paradoxically, it turned out that although it comes from the dry altiplano of the Andes, it grows equally well in wet weather. As a result it thrived in the mild, damp weather conditions in the west of Ireland when other crops like cereals did not. Moreover, in Ireland the potato was unaffected by the damaging leaf curl disease, which would cause such trouble in England in the late 18th century. The reason for this relative immunity was that the aphid

Potato leaves damaged by the potato late blight fungus (*Phytophthora infestans*). This fungus can seriously damage potato crops, and was the cause of the tragic potato famine in Ireland.

Science Photo Library

that transmitted leaf curl did not relish the strong winds and heavy rain of the west and south-west of Ireland. Another reason for the success of the crop is that frost is rare in these areas and severe frost almost unknown. By 1780, as a result of all these factors working together, the potato had become the staple crop in Ireland.

However, the system of land management in Ireland was appalling. Most of the peasantry could not aspire to ownership. The best that could be hoped for was to be a tenant with a small farm or smallholding, which rarely provided anything more than a subsistence income. To compound this problem various factors contributed to a dramatic increase in population from around 4 million in 1785 to around 8 million in 1825, just 40 years later, with the potato supporting this large population. This combination of an uncontrolled expansion of the population and reliance on a single staple crop, only one variety of which was grown, was a powder keg waiting to explode.

The explosion, or rather the infestation, came in the 1840s. This devastating problem would prove to be a fungus called 'late blight' or 'black blight' (*Phytophthora infestans*). The outbreak of blight appears to have originated in Philadelphia in 1843, and then to have passed to Europe in ships loaded with fertiliser. It was first reported in England on the Isle of Wight in August 1845 and reached Ireland in September of the same year. Each fungal lesion (the dark spot) on a leaf can produce immense numbers of spores – as many as 300,000 – over the course of four or five days. The spores are readily spread by the wind and as a result a whole field can be devastated in a very short period of time. The leaves and stems of the plant rapidly decay and die.

Ireland and the Potato Famine

The underground tubers go black and turn into a foul-smelling pulp.

The Great Famine, as it was known, between the years 1845 and 1852 would cause the deaths of around a million people and also result in the emigration of a further million and a half. It would take 50 years for Irish agriculture to recover. The Irish population rapidly became seriously malnourished and as a result diseases of many types, including scurvy and beriberi (lack of Vitamin C and B1 respectively) and the infectious diseases cholera, dysentery, typhus and relapsing fever, took their opportunity to strike. Several successive potato crop failures occurred between 1845 and 1847 and then in 1848 outright collapse ensued. Mass starvation was accompanied by mass eviction instigated largely by the absentee landlords who remained in Britain. It is estimated that between 1845 and 1852 about half a million people were evicted from their homes or farms as they were unable to pay their rents.

Gradually, over a number of years the situation was brought under control, largely thanks to the introduction of new varieties of potato which in the short term remained relatively resistant to blight. However, the fungus remains a constant problem, with farmers in the United Kingdom alone spending around £60 million every year on pesticides to protect their crops from the infestation. In 2012 scientists began trials on a genetically modified potato in an attempt to create a variety that would be blight-resistant without the need for chemical spraying. In early 2014 it was announced that all such GM potatoes were so far proving fully resistant against the blight, although no one can say how long this will remain the case.

Science Photo Library

A comparison between wild (on the right) and domestic (on the left) potatoes. The tubers of the wild species are small and unfit for consumption but the genes are often valuable for contributing positive traits to commercial potatoes.

dependent on the potato, and as a result the country would not be as vulnerable as Ireland to the impending nemesis of the 1840s.

In 1914, when the Germans initiated the submarine blockade of Britain at the beginning of the First World War, the agricultural economy of the country became vitally dependent on the production of the potato. In 1916, when the British potato crop failed, there was widespread malnutrition and serious outbreaks of scurvy. By 1917, the convoy system and other measures put in place against the blockade began to overcome the threat from beneath the waves, but it had been a narrow squeak as the British had neglected to learn the lessons of the Great Famine in Ireland.

The Potato as a Poison

Root vegetables were regarded with suspicion for centuries and thought of as evil in many parts of Europe in the 16th and 17th centuries. They were said to provoke menstruation and lust in women and overproduction of sperm in men. Even worse, it was held that such vegetables could encourage the spread of infectious disease such as leprosy. The potato was also thought to be poisonous because of its resemblance to the mandrake and deadly nightshade. This suspicion was in part justified because in certain circumstances the potato is indeed toxic.

Farmers knew for generations that livestock, in particular cattle and pigs, could be poisoned by potatoes, particularly if the potatoes had gone green or were sprouting at the 'eyes'. The symptoms included drowsiness, weakness, vomiting and finally paralysis. The animals would also frequently show signs of a skin disease commonly known as 'potato eruption', with lesions on the lower abdomen and inner parts of the thigh which could take several weeks to clear. Similar skin lesions occur in humans and can aid the diagnosis of potato poisoning.

Several important outbreaks of potato poisoning have occurred in humans, including one in Glasgow in 1918 and another in London in 1978. These large outbreaks tend to run to a pattern, with most of the victims mildly affected and a few seriously poisoned. The most common symptoms are vomiting and diarrhoea and there are rarely any fatalities.

Potato poisoning is caused by the main toxic compounds in the potato: the alkaloids solanine and chaconine. However, as their function is to protect the plant from predators, they cause the potato to have a bitter taste which warns the potential consumers (largely beetles and caterpillars) that it is inadvisable to eat the plant. This danger persists in some modern potato varieties, such as Home Guard, Rocket and British Queen, all of which are poisonous in the early part of their maturation.

These alkaloids are resistant to cooking and may stay in the body for several days and so cooking the potato will not necessarily reduce the toxicity. Most potatoes bought commercially or

α-Solanine

Solatunine

$C_{45}H_{73}NO_{15}$

in retail outlets will contain low concentrations of solanine (4–10 mg per 100 g of dry weight), but if the concentration is greater than 20 mg per 100 g then the tubers present a toxic hazard. The highest concentration of alkaloid occurs just under the skin of the potato and in areas of high metabolic activity such as the eyes. There is normally a marked difference in the amount of alkaloid between the concentration in the peel and the underlying flesh, and so peeling potatoes makes them much less likely to contain any of the harmful alkaloid. To be on the safe side, however, green or sprouting potatoes should be discarded. Other poisonous compounds, called steroid saponins, also occur in the tuber. These destroy red blood cells and may also contribute to the overall toxicity of the potato on the digestive tract and other systems.

The elimination of 'poison' in the potato means reducing by a factor of 15 to 20 the concentration of the alkaloid. Some of the reduction in poison may have occurred by lucky accident, normal biological variance or even mutation; these might then have been selected by the Andean growers who went on to propagate them. However, reversion to type – the process by which plants that have been changed by selection and cultivation can return to their original nature – may occur in sprouting tubers of any variety, allowing solanine to be produced. Other Andean tribes dealt with the poisonous alkaloids in a different way. They mixed the bitter potatoes with clay before they ate them; the clay absorbed the poison and allowed it to pass through the gut.

The death's-head hawkmoth (*Acherontia atropos*) is known for the skull-like marking on its thorax and the fact that it lets out a high-pitched squeak when disturbed. It is further remarkable because its caterpillar feeds on the potato but is immune to solanine.

Science Photo Library

Mr Potato and the Dagger of Despair

In France, the popularisation of the potato as a staple foodstuff was largely thanks to the unremitting efforts of a single individual, the pharmacist Antoine Auguste Parmentier (1737–1813). Over a period of 50 years he became known as

A posthumous portrait in oil of Antoine Parmentier, the man who introduced the potato to France, by François Dumont, which hangs in the Palace of Versailles.

Bridgeman Images

Monsieur Cartoufle (Mr Potato) as a result of his single-minded obsession. The French first called the potato *cartoufle* (similar to the German *Kartoffel*) before it later came to be known as *pomme de terre* (literally 'apple of the earth'). After initial training as a pharmacist, Parmentier joined the army. Captured by the Prussians in the Seven Years' War (1756–1763), he later claimed that he survived his incarceration by living on a diet composed solely of potatoes.

When he was repatriated to France he spent the next 40 years promoting and popularising the potato. He was on good terms with the royal family, in particular Louis XV and Louis XVI. The former appointed him to a sinecure in order that he would be able to pursue his campaign. On one occasion he acted as host at a dinner for Arthur Young, the English agriculturalist, at which the menu consisted of 20 separate courses each based on the potato. Arthur Young was not impressed and commented that the French spent too much time on theory and not enough on practice.

When Louis XVI came to the throne, Parmentier continued his good relationship with the court and persuaded the King and

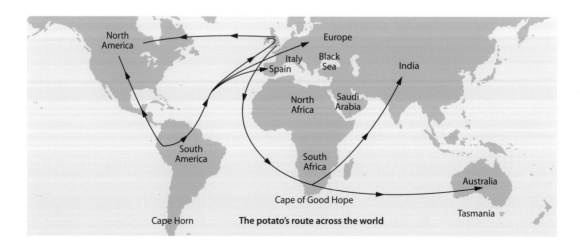

The potato's route across the world

his wife Queen Marie-Antoinette to wear buttonholes of the attractive lilac flower of the potato. The King subsequently awarded him a medal for his continued efforts. In 1789, just before the Revolution, Parmentier carried out experiments on the tubers of the potato and concluded that they did not contain any dangerous or soporific substances.

Then, on 14 July of the same year, the Revolution started with all its accompanying mayhem and bloodshed. Amongst all the committees that were set up by the revolutionaries was one called the Commission on Subsistence and Provisions. This group was instructed to try to define methods to prevent the recurrent famines that had plagued France for years. Parmentier submitted a pamphlet which was gratefully accepted by the committee, who made the grandiose claim that the potato 'would plunge the dagger of despair into the hearts of any would-be malefactors'.[1] It was the patriotic duty of any Republican to grow the potato on land previously owned by the aristocrats. Areas such as parks, gardens and forests were to be seized by the people for the purpose.

Parmentier was lucky to have avoided the guillotine. He had been closely associated with the royal family and, indeed, had received a medal from Louis XVI. This was for him a dangerous time. Later, when Napoleon assumed power, Parmentier's advice on the potato would again prove useful. In 1806, Napoleon, as Emperor, issued the Decree of Berlin which among other things declared an economic embargo on the United Kingdom. This provoked a counter-blockade by the Royal Navy that immediately aggravated food shortages throughout Europe. Parmentier once again encouraged the French peasantry to plant potatoes and production of the tubers rose sharply. As the end of his life approached, Parmentier was showered with awards including the Légion d'Honneur and was also appointed Minister for Health. He died in 1813 before the fall of Napoleon. Now the name Parmentier is remembered in names of such dishes as *crêpes Parmentier*, a pancake dish made from potatoes, and *hâchis Parmentier*, the French equivalent of shepherd's pie.

We have followed the potato from the High Andes of Peru to the dining rooms of Europe, a journey punctuated by disaster and widespread hostility. However, the potato is now a staple food crop and has become part of the social history of Britain through dishes such as the humble baked potato, fish and chips, and sausage and mash. As we pick up our weekly bag of spuds in the supermarket, we should pause for a moment to reflect on this long trail of triumph and disaster and give thanks to all those who have made a significant contribution to the adoption of the humble tuber. In Braunlage, a small town in the Lower Saxony area of Germany, a large stone monument honours the potato, a reminder of the time in the 18th century when 12 acres of land was cleared to cultivate potatoes for the first time in an attempt to find a solution to the dire economic situation of the starving locals. The monument bears the inscription 'the greatest antidote against starvation'. It is no less than the tuberous *Solanum* deserves.

Plate 56
第五十六圖

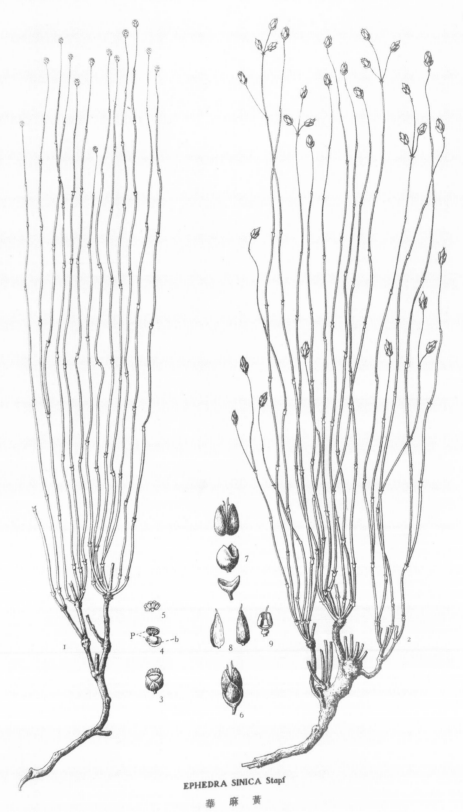

EPHEDRA SINICA Stapf

華 麻 黃

9 – Ma Huang (*Ephedra sinica*): A Chinese Treatment for Asthma

Ephedra sinica, known to the ancient world for its medicinal uses, has in modern times played a twin role. Its active alkaloid ephedrine has been used successfully to treat the symptoms of the common cold, asthma and hay fever, although now its use has largely been supplanted by more effective drugs. Ephedrine was also used widely in herbal weight-loss supplements, until the late 1990s saw increasing concerns regarding its toxicity and consequent health risks. Reports of serious side-effects and even fatalities associated with the drug led to the eventual ban, in 2004, of dietary supplements containing the alkaloid. Despite its official ban, it is nonetheless still used as a performance-enhancing drug by certain athletes and as one of the raw ingredients of the highly addictive recreational drug methamphetamine.

The Ephedraceae are an ancient plant group belonging to the gymnosperms (literally 'naked seeds'), the non-flowering plants that include pines, monkey puzzles and *Ginkgo*. There are some 45 species of *Ephedra* distributed all over the world, particularly in coastal and subalpine areas. They are small shrubs with slender angular and ridged branches whose leaves are reduced to membranous scales to reduce transpiration in the arid, windy areas where they exist. Plants are typically dioecious, that is the male and female reproductive organs are carried on different plants. The female apparatus is an ovule surrounded by fleshy bracts. At maturity these bracts merge to form a structure like a pine cone, although in many species, they are fleshy to aid dispersal. Male cones are grouped in yellow catkin-like cones.

The plants vary widely in their production of alkaloids. Some, such as the American and Chilean species, produce hardly any of the active principles. The only common species in Europe is *Ephedra distachya*, the woody horsetail, which has its habitat on the Atlantic coast. It too produces little alkaloid. In contrast, the Chinese and Indian species of *Ephedra* make significant amounts of the active compounds. These species include *E. sinica* and *E. equisetina* in China and *E. intermedia* and *E. gerardiana* in India. The Chinese and Indian species became a major commercial source of the alkaloid ephedrine and were shipped all over the world.

The History of Ephedra

Traditional Chinese medicine has recognised *Ephedra sinica* since ancient times. According to Chinese mythology, the Emperor Shennong (born c. 2800 BC) taught the Chinese people basic agriculture, allowing them to discover that rice and other cereals were good to eat and that some plants appeared to be able to heal disease. Shennong (literally 'the Divine Farmer') also tasted hundreds of medicinal herbs, describing their healing properties and effects, and thus became the father of Chinese herbal medicine. When this knowledge eventually became a formal written work, it was named *Shennong Bencao Jing* (*The Divine Farmer's Herb Root Classic*) in honour of Shennong and underpinned the work of many apothethecaries who followed in the centuries to come. The Divine Farmer was succeeded by Huangdi, the Yellow

Emperor (c. 2696–2598 BC). He and his senior ministers are said to have produced the *Huangdi Neijing* (*The Yellow Emperor's Inner Classic*), regarded as another key source for all Chinese medicine and eventually codified in 100 BC. In this text Ma Huang is mentioned for the first time as a possible treatment for chest complaints.

Many apothecaries worked over the centuries to refine the Yellow Emperor's work, among whom one of the greatest was Li Shizhen (AD 1518–1593), another esteemed physician. His *Bencao Gangmu* (*Compendium of Materia Medica*) comprises 52 volumes and describes almost 1,900 drugs. Among these preparations 350 were derived from minerals, 443 from animals and 1,099 from plants. Li Shizhen spent 30 years on this project, creating what was the best pharmacopoeia available at the time, far exceeding comparable works in European languages in both scope and illustrations. It was translated into Latin, Japanese, French, German and English. From this work *Ephedra sinica* came to be known as a stimulator of the circulation, a diaphoretic to promote sweating and an antipyretic to reduce fever. It was also believed to be useful in treating coughs and as a result the stem became an important ingredient of many cough remedies. At the end of the 16th century the dried stems were exported to Japan, a trade which was to play an important part in stimulating the interest of Japanese physicians and chemists in the plant some 300 years later.

A woodcut from an edition of *Shennong Bencao Jing* engraved in the Wanli reign period of the Ming dynasty showing Shennong, the Divine Farmer.

A woodcut of the Yellow Emperor. It is in the texts from his reign that Ma Huang is first mentioned as a possible treatment for asthma.

Other species of *Ephedra* (later recognised as *E. pachyclada* and *E. intermedia*) were thought to have medicinal value and were found in Greece, Russia, India and the Americas. Various religious groups in India used them in their ceremonies to produce feelings of exhilaration. These species of *Ephedra* act as central nervous excitants as a result of the rapid passage of ephedrine from the blood into the brain. This stimulates neurons in the limbic system of the brain, which also controls part of the hypothalamus (the part of the brain that supports a variety of functions, including emotion). As the preparations used by Indian religious sects also contained ethyl alcohol, it is impossible to know how much of the ecstatic experience was due to alcohol, how much to ephedrine and how much to the interaction between the two. In the Americas, a number of other species were known to indigenous peoples. These were later classified as *Ephedra antisyphilitica*, *E. californica* and *E. nevadensis*.

They were thought to act against syphilis and gonorrhoea and were either applied directly to the genital organs or taken by mouth. *E. nevadensis* had some interesting vernacular names such as 'Mormon tea' and 'whorehouse tea'. It seems likely that in the brothels it was thought to stimulate sexual excitement as well as to protect against sexually transmitted diseases. As it contained no ephedrine it is highly unlikely that it had any effect at all.

The Discovery and Isolation of Ephedrine

The Japanese scientist Nagai Nagayoshi (1844–1929) is the central figure in the first era of scientific work on ephedrine. He studied medicine at the Dutch Academy in Nagasaki and completed his studies in Tokyo. He then travelled to Berlin in 1871 and worked there for 12 years with the famous chemist August Wilhelm von Hofmann (1818–1892).

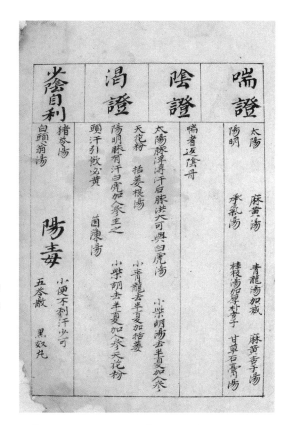

A Chinese medication chart for asthma from a manuscript dated the first year of the Zhengyuan reign period of the Yuan dynasty (1341). Part of the text states that asthma is characterised by shortness of breath. Greater Yang asthma is generally treated with *Ephedra* decoction or Variant Blue-Green Dragon decoction.

Nagayoshi returned to Japan in 1883 and began to work on *Ephedra*. In 1885, he isolated ephedrine, which can exist in two forms, the left-handed variety l-ephedrine and the right-handed d-ephedrine. He passed his pure preparation of l-ephedrine to a colleague who, in 1887, undertook studies on its pharmacological properties in various animal preparations. He reported that it was too toxic to the circulation to be used in the whole animal or human, but that it might prove useful in dilating the pupil. Its ability to do so was readily reversible with time, in contrast to the prolonged and possibly dangerous action of the tropane alkaloids atropine and homatropine, commonly used in the treatment of diseases of the eye. This use of ephedrine as an agent to dilate the pupil did not, however, gain general acceptance.

There was then a gap of 30 years in which ephedrine remained in limbo, until scientists in Japan re-examined the actions of the alkaloid. To their surprise, they found that l-ephedrine was capable of raising the blood pressure and accelerating the heart. In these actions it resembled tyramine and adrenaline, which had been identified in the intervening years. Moreover, the scientists also noticed that ephedrine, like adrenaline, was capable of relaxing the smooth muscles in the bronchi (the main passageways into the chest). They therefore suggested that it could have therapeutic potential in the treatment of bronchial asthma. Following this work, a medicine containing ephedrine, named Asthmatol, was marketed in northern China for the treatment of asthma, but, having little or no success, it fell into disuse.

In the early 1920s, ephedrine was virtually unknown in the West. When Ko Kuei Chen (1898–1988) and Carl F Schmidt (1893–1965) took up their posts in 1920 as lecturers at the Peking Union Medical College they decided to investigate promising drugs from the Chinese pharmacopoeia. A local apothecary suggested that Ma Huang might be worth a further look, although no one was aware of the previous findings. After investigation Chen and Schmidt came to a number of important conclusions about *Ephedra sinica* and ephedrine, which were seen as marking a major breakthrough in

the field of pharmacology. They found that the main actions of ephedrine are on the bronchi and the heart.

Adrenaline (extracted from the bovine adrenal gland) had proven to be an effective treatment for asthma but it had substantial drawbacks. Ephedrine proved superior. As a dry powder, or even in solution, it is stable for considerably longer periods than adrenaline. Some patients who could not tolerate adrenaline injections could be effectively treated with oral ephedrine. As a result of their findings Chen and Schmidt decided to send samples of *Ephedra* and ephedrine to Thomas Miller, a noted respiratory physician in the United States. He was able to show definite therapeutic effects in dilating the bronchi in order to treat asthma. Moreover, ephedrine seemed able to stop severe constriction of the bronchi when given in the early stage of an attack.

The first publications on asthma in the United States stimulated what might be called an ephedrine gold rush. Every American paediatrician and respiratory physician wanted to get hold of this 'new' plant or its active alkaloid. Several patents were filed in the United States and Europe for the preparation of the plant extract and for the synthesis of the active alkaloid. Over the same period exports of the plant from China to the United States increased substantially. One American pharmaceutical company tried to control the market by buying all the supplies of *Ephedra* in China; this bold attempt failed, however, when supplies of the active extracts of the Indian species of *Ephedra* became more generally available.

By the mid-1930s ephedrine had become established throughout the Western world as a reliable treatment for asthma. Primitive inhalers were developed to deliver the drug, but they proved unsatisfactory as they failed to give a measured dose, a problem which was only solved in the 1960s with a new generation of breath-actuated metred-dose inhalers. Two further problems arose in the 1930s. First,

L-Ephedrine

(1*R*,2*S*)-form

$C_{10}H_{15}NO$

Ephedra sinica, one of the *Ephedra* species that makes a significant amount of the active compound ephedrine.

it emerged that *Ephedra* extracts contained significant amounts of its mirror image isomer d-pseudoephedrine. Anxiety arose as to what effects, if any, pseudoephedrine had on the clinical effects of pure 1-ephedrine, although it later transpired that there were none of any real concern. The second problem emerged in 1937 when the Japanese invaded northern China and

A Rybar Standard Inhaler No 1, which consisted of a Bakelite mouthpiece, plastic reservoir and atomiser-style rubber ball for squeezing to administer 'asthma inhalant therapy'.

gradually advanced south. Supplies of *Ephedra* were in jeopardy and shortages occurred. As a result, South Dakota State College in the United States successfully initiated a scheme to grow *E. sinica*. In addition, India increased the acreage of *E. sinica* under cultivation, and a new synthesis for ephedrine from basic chemicals was developed. Ultimately the supplies from China were no longer needed.

With the widespread use and availability of ephedrine either in pure form or in compound tablets it gradually became clear that the alkaloid was more toxic than had first been supposed. This was particularly true if it was taken on a long-term preventative basis. The other dangers of ephedrine in acute overdose are many and various, but those that are life-threatening affect the central nervous and cardiovascular systems. These include convulsions, high blood pressure and fatal abnormalities of heart rhythm. Because individuals can become habituated to the effects of ephedrine on the central nervous system, they need to take ever higher doses of the alkaloid to produce the same stimulatory effects, increasing the chance of their dosage becoming toxic. These concerns, together with the development of other drugs, led to the decline in the use of ephedrine from the early 1950s, and it rapidly became obsolete.

As ephedrine declined as a therapeutic drug, crude *Ephedra* was still being imported into the Americas from China and India. In many South American countries it is still widely available as an over-the-counter medication for coughs, asthma and bronchitis. It gained a reputation as a 'street drug', which soon became as cheap and easily available as cocaine and amphetamine. It was valued in particular as a preparation to give a quick 'high' and was also thought to strengthen muscular performance in athletes and bodybuilders, as well as aiding weight loss. Accordingly it began to be used as a performance-enhancing drug by sportspeople of all types. If the substance was detected in their urine they could always argue that they had taken the preparation for asthma, bronchitis or the common cold. All sportspeople are now tested for the presence of ephedrine in the blood or urine.

Ephedrine and Methamphetamine

Towards the end of the 20th century a final twist emerged in the long saga of *Ephedra* and ephedrine. The drug began to be used in the illicit manufacture of the powerful stimulant methamphetamine (known as crystal meth). Methamphetamine can be synthesised in a simple one-step procedure by a chemical reduction of ephedrine. *Ephedra* and ephedrine were widely available over the counter in North and South America, leading to the growth of two sorts of laboratory: small criminal 'mom and pop' set-ups and large criminal 'superlabs', most often located in Mexico and on the west coast of the United States.

These factors have resulted in an epidemic of addiction to crystal meth in certain regions of North America, which has resulted in many cases of acute psychosis as well as extensive damage to the nervous system. In addition, large numbers of people have been admitted to hospital with burns sustained in making crystal meth in a confined space. Unlike cocaine, methamphetamine does not have to be transported long distances from South America to the United States, making interdiction difficult or even impossible, particularly in the case of the small laboratories. The situation is reminiscent of the 'moonshine' stills in the days of alcohol prohibition. Crystal meth is very widely available on the street and is now cheaper than cocaine.

The United States and Mexican governments are attempting to arrest the supplies of *Ephedra* from Asia but so far have had limited success. They are also trying to ban pharmacies from selling *Ephedra* or ephedrine over the counter. This again has proved to be extremely difficult, particularly in Latin America. *Ephedra*, once used as the drug of choice for the treatment of asthma in the 1930s and 1940s, is now helping to fuel the fire of a major outbreak of drug addiction in North America.

Methamphetamine, 'crystal meth', a central nervous system stimulant drug similar to amphetamine and responsible for many deaths. The drug, which can be synthesised from ephedrine, increases alertness, concentration and energy, and in high doses may induce euphoria and enhance self-esteem.

Science Photo Library

The Death of an Oriole

A famous case which shows the dangers of ephedrine occurred in 2003 when a young baseball pitcher from the Baltimore Orioles embarked on a course of a nutritional supplement which was later shown to contain ephedrine. In the middle of a training session on an unpleasantly hot day he collapsed, was rushed to hospital and subsequently died. The autopsy revealed that he had suffered heatstroke, complicated by renal and cardiac failure, together with swelling in his brain. A high concentration of ephedrine was detected in his blood. High temperature is a known complication of an ephedrine overdose, probably because of its action on the brain's temperature control mechanisms, which then act to prevent general dilation of the blood vessels and sweating. The sudden death of this fit young man caused a storm of media interest. Anger gripped the baseball world when it turned out that he had taken the toxic plant *Ephedra sinica* without knowing that it could be poisonous. When it also transpired that it was perfectly legal to buy the plant as a constituent of over-the-counter nutritional supplements, the incident came to be regarded as a national tragedy. In a short time baseball, and other athletic authorities, banned *Ephedra*. Somewhat belatedly, the Food and Drug Administration

Oriole Park at Camden Yards, the home of the Baltimore Orioles. The tragic death of a member of the team raised the issue of the dangers of *Ephedra* usage.

reviewed its previous relaxation of the rules and banned *Ephedra* in so-called nutritional supplements. The sales of these supplements fell dramatically for several years.

It was discovered by the Canadian and Mexican authorities that similar deaths had occurred in their respective countries in people taking *Ephedra*. The certified causes of death were either cardiac failure, hyperthermia or both. Although it is impossible to know exactly how many people were killed worldwide by *Ephedra* in nutritional supplements, the figure probably runs into the hundreds. Since the 1930s, studies had shown that ephedrine in overdose could produce potentially fatal cardiac failure, hyperthermia and convulsions, making this an entirely avoidable tragedy.

So ends the story of Ma Huang which started five millennia ago in China. It was featured in many Chinese herbals before the plant was classified as *Ephedra sinica*. The discovery of ephedrine is a sound illustration of the process by which a plant known in folklore to be active is clearly identified and then named using the Linnaean binomial system. The active substance, in this case ephedrine, is then isolated and synthesised before further work confirms its pharmacological and therapeutic activity, together with its toxic risk. Ephedrine still has its uses in dilating the pupil and as a nasal decongestant; however, as an oral drug for asthma it has all but disappeared. A valuable therapeutic drug for the 1930s and 1940s has become a scourge in the 21st century through its inclusion in dietary supplements and as a source of a highly addictive and dangerous street drug. It would unfortunately appear that this ancient healer has now turned killer.

W.Müller n. d.Nat.

Digitalis purpurea L.

10 – The Foxglove *(Digitalis purpurea)*: William Withering and the Treatment of the Dropsy

The foxglove is a familiar, common and attractive plant, popular as an ornamental. Drugs prepared from the dried leaves of the plant are still used medically to treat heart conditions although in recent years they have, to a certain degree, been replaced with other medicines which are considered to be safer. Despite its use in medicine, *Digitalis* is toxic and ingestion of too much of the leaf, or indeed of any part of the plant, causes harm to the body and may even be fatal. It was the English scientist William Withering (1741–1799) who was responsible for introducing the foxglove leaf into the armamentarium of the physician. He also worked to establish the correct dose, particularly pertinent in the case of this plant as its therapeutic dose and its toxic dose are very similar. Withering was a true polymath and his far-reaching achievements are a fine example of the massive progress made in the field of science during the age of Enlightenment in the 17th and 18th centuries.

The foxglove genus belongs to the family Plantaginaceae. There are around 20 species of biennial or perennial herbs in the genus, with some of the more familiar including *Digitalis purpurea* (the common foxglove), *D. lutea*, *D. grandiflora* and *D. parviflora*. Only the first of these is native to the UK and northern Europe, with *D. lutea* found in western and central Europe and Russia, and *D. lanata* in Austria and Greece. The plants usually have a basal rosette of leaves from which a tall raceme of showy tubular flowers arises; the colour varies according to the species but can range from purple and pink through to white and yellow. The flowers also sometimes have various marks and blotch-like spots, thought to be nectar guides for visiting insects.

The Foxglove in History and Mythology

The Latin name *digitalis* means 'like a finger' and refers to the way the flower can fit neatly over a finger, like a glove. The etymology of the common name foxglove is much less certain. There are several theories, the

A portrait of the German botanist Leonhart Fuchs from the frontispiece of his 1542 *Herbal*, in which he described the foxglove.

simplest of which suggests that it comes from an old legend that foxes wore the flowers on their paws to deaden the noise as they raided poultry farms by night. Another possibility – although rather a remote one – is that the name is derived from Leonhart Fuchs (1501–1566), the German botanist who in 1542 gave the plant its Latin name in his herbal entitled *De Historia Stirpium Commentarii Insignes* (*Notable Commentaries on the History of Plants*). Fuchs is the German word for fox and 'Fuchs' glove' might easily have become 'foxglove' over the years. However, there is some evidence that the plant was known as the foxglove centuries before Fuchs was alive. It seems more likely that the original name was 'folks' glove'. 'Little folk' was a term used to refer to fairies and the bells of the flowers were thought to be a good place for fairies to hide. The toxicity of the plant is perhaps also a reflection of the often sinister nature of fairies as portrayed in folk tales.

Medici/Mary Evans

The foxglove, then, was long bound up with superstition and folklore; it was supposedly used in casting magic spells and in communicating with woodland fairies and spirits. Common names for the plant include fairy's gloves, fairy bells, fairy thimbles, witches' fingers, lion's mouth, dead men's bells and floppy dock. It is found even as far back as Roman mythology: the goddess Juno, who looked after the women of Rome, discovered that her husband Jupiter's daughter Minerva had sprung direct from her husband's head. Despondent at her failure to produce a child, she sought help from Flora, the goddess of flowers and springtime. Flora put a foxglove flower onto Juno's thumb and then touched her stomach, after which Juno went to the seashore and gave birth to Mars.

The Foxglove as a Healer

Modern research has taught us that the leaves, flowers and roots of the foxglove contain many pharmacologically active compounds, including digoxin, acetyldigoxin, digitoxin and acetyldigitoxin. These chemicals are known collectively as the cardiac glycosides and are used to treat a variety of heart conditions by slowing and regularising the heartbeat and increasing blood flow to the kidneys, so causing the patient to produce a large volume of urine and thus get rid of excess fluid in the body, making the heart work more efficiently.

To examine the history of how the foxglove has come to be used in therapeutic medicine, we must turn our attention to William Withering, who was the first to recognise that digitalis was the active ingredient of the foxglove plant, used by traditional herbalists in the treatment of heart conditions. Not only had the *Digitalis* plant been known and used

An illustration from the 1935 children's book *Magic Flowers* by Margaret Tarrant, a perfect example of the appeal of the foxglove and its association with superstition, folklore and particularly fairies.

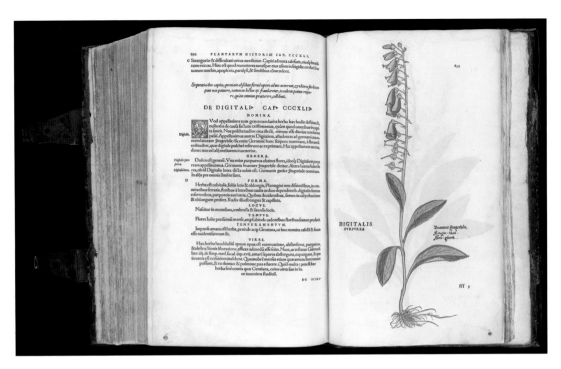

The illustration and description of the foxglove from Fuchs' *Herbal* of 1542.

as a folk medicine for centuries, but classic descriptions had been given by the Greek physicians Dioscorides (c. AD 40–90) and Galen (c. AD 129–200). Leonhart Fuchs, in *De Historia Stirpium Commentarii Insignes*, recommended the use of the foxglove to treat dropsy (the former term for oedema, or swelling in the soft tissues caused by excess fluid). He also advised that it could be used to treat sore throats and catarrh and that the leaves could be used as a dressing for skin ulcers. Withering knew of Fuchs' work but his interest in the plant was further stimulated when he met a 'wise woman' in Shropshire who used the foxglove as one component of her medicine to treat dropsy. The concoction contained at least 20 different herbs but, according to Withering, 'it was not difficult for one conversant in these subjects to perceive that the active herb could be no other than the Foxglove'.[1]

Withering's specific contribution was to put the use of *Digitalis* on a proper scientific footing, thereby eliminating much of its

A portrait of William Withering by Carl Frederick von Breda. Von Breda painted various members of the Lunar Society during a visit to Birmingham in 1792. In this portrait Withering holds foxgloves in his hand while by his elbow are volumes he has written.

folklore and superstition. He established that the dried powdered leaf of the plant was five times as effective as the fresh leaf. It was also better to dry the leaf than to boil it, as boiling seemed to destroy some of the active principles. He went on to study 163 patients with dropsy and recorded his results carefully, noting that a brisk increase in urinary flow often heralded the patient's recovery. From this protracted study he realised for the first time the paramount importance of the dose administered. Some patients who appeared to have similar symptoms did not respond to *Digitalis*, for example those who also had a tight swelling of the abdomen, indicating that they may have had cirrhosis of the liver. Withering also described clearly, for the first time, the important side effects of the drug, which included nausea, vomiting, diarrhoea and green or yellow vision. Interestingly, the artist Vincent van Gogh used digoxin to treat his epilepsy; it has been suggested that the prevalence of the colour yellow in his later paintings may well be explained by visual problems he suffered from taking too high a dose.

Digoxin

Digoxigenin 3-tridigitoxoside

$C_{41}H_{64}O_{14}$

Claims had also been made that the plant was effective in treating tuberculosis and epilepsy but Withering was sceptical about such statements. He had no clear idea how the drug worked to 'scatter' the swelling in the soft tissue but he suspected that the increase in urine flow produced might play

The title page and some of the content of Withering's text *An account of the foxglove.*

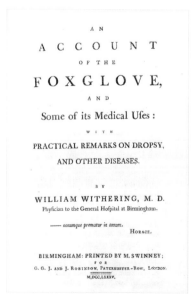

William Withering: the English Linnaeus

Quite apart from his work on *Digitalis* William Withering was a fascinating character. Over 200 years after his death, most physicians are aware of his pioneering work on the foxglove but few know of his other distinguished efforts in botany, geology and chemistry. He was an active member of the Lunar Society, a learned society based in the Midlands. In 1776, he published *A Botanical Arrangement of all the Vegetables Growing Naturally in Great Britain.* This book contained much new information on plants as food and on those that are poisonous to livestock. There was also an introduction to techniques for the drying and preservation of specimens. This was the first British publication using the Linnaean system and it was widely welcomed. His analytical approach concludes with a broadside against superstition in the passage in which he states 'we shall sooner obtain the end proposed if we take up the ancient herbalist, but build only upon the basis of accurate and well considered experiments'.[2] He took his own advice to heart in his work on the foxglove.

On the strength of his sustained record in botany he was elected to the Fellowship of the Linnean Society. Subsequently the plant *Witheringia solanacea* was named after him. Withering was meticulous, almost obsessive, in his observation and recording of plants, earning himself the nickname 'The English Linnaeus'. His work on flowering plants was largely derived from other authorities, but that on algae and agarics did break new ground. In addition, he pursued many other miscellaneous interests including the manufacture of stainless steel for scalpels, the history of Stonehenge, the effects of lightning, methods for inhaling volatile substances and those for making arsenical compounds more soluble (arsenic was becoming prominent in the treatment of syphilis and skin diseases). He also developed interests in geology and mineralogy, analysing 12 different sorts of marl (a type of mud rich in lime) from the Midlands to determine their calcium content and to establish how much quicklime each would generate on heating. Through this their suitability for the improvement of agricultural land could be assessed.

Perhaps his major contribution to mineralogy, however, was his work on Terra Ponderosa, a heavy ore found abundantly on Alston Moor in Cumberland. Withering noticed its great weight and conjectured that it might contain a new element. He thus embarked on a series of experiments to characterise its

By permission of the Linnean Society of London

Witheringia solanacea, the plant named in honour of William Withering and his contribution to botany.

William Withering

Science Photo Library

A coloured scanning electron micrograph (SEM) of crystals of witherite, or barium carbonate, named after William Withering who carried out the initial work on its isolation.

constituents, but was unable to isolate it. Following further work by the Swedish chemist Jöns Jacob Berzelius (1779–1848), it was the latter's contemporary Humphry Davy (1778–1829) who, in 1808, isolated barium using electrolysis. The mineral was named witherite after William Withering by the German geologist Abraham Gottlob Werner (1749–1817), who spent many years working on a practical classification system of minerals.

Withering developed an irregular fever in 1776. His next 20 years were punctuated by attacks of coughing (probably from chronic bronchitis and tuberculosis), breathlessness and fever. He died on 6 October 1799 and was buried at Edgbaston Old Church. Later, a magnificent epitaph was erected in the church. The verse inscribed on the monument begins:

While heaven born genius drops
on earth a tear,
and Science drooping mourns
o'er Withering's bier.

At the base of the epitaph on the right is the foxglove *Digitalis* and on the left *Witheringia*, a fitting tribute to his work in both medicine and botany.

a part. He also thought that it might be an effective treatment for an irregular heartbeat but he did not make a clear connection between the heart, dropsy and fluid retention. As a result of these uncertainties other physicians were to use *Digitalis* inappropriately: in too large a dose or in conditions where it was ineffective. These problems would not be resolved for a further century, until such time as histopathology and electrocardiography became established. Nevertheless, Withering's resulting 1785 publication, *An account of the foxglove and some of its medical uses; with practical remarks on the dropsy, and some other diseases*, was a notable advance based entirely on clinical observation and it changed the face of medical practice for ever.

In the modern era digoxin has largely been replaced by other, more effective, drugs such as furosemide, a diuretic, and amiodarone, a more powerful drug used to control abnormalities of the heart rhythm. During the 1930s, however, it was still in common use as a treatment; at the time most of the digoxin used in Britain was imported from Europe, principally Russia. At the outbreak of World War II these supplies were suddenly cut off, causing a serious shortage. The British government called upon the public to help resolve the crisis by collecting the leaves of the purple foxglove and drying them slowly in warm areas of their houses. Arrangements were made by pharmaceutical companies to collect them so that they could be further processed to create the pure glycoside digoxin. During this nationwide search for the purple foxglove, a superb colony was detected near the top of Wenlock Edge in Shropshire. It is presumed that the alkali had been washed out of the rock at this level, leaving a highly acid environment in which the foxglove flourished.

The Toxicity of the Foxglove

Poisoning from *Digitalis* can occur in cases of overdose and sometimes in patients with other health problems or simply a lower tolerance to the drug. This latter is particularly dangerous as the levels of *Digitalis* in the patient's blood will appear to be within the normal range. Poisoning from the foxglove plant is relatively rare and happens primarily when young children accidentally ingest the plant. There was, however, an infamous case in 2008 in Jefferson County, Colorado, when a woman attempted to murder her husband by including foxglove leaves in the salad she had prepared for his dinner. The woman's husband, a police-dog handler, was suspicious when his wife called him at work to tell him she had made him a special meal, as they had argued the night before. The salad she served him tasted bitter and so he did not eat it all. He became apprehensive when his wife would not let their young daughter eat from his plate, something she often did. Checking the fridge after the meal he found no sign of the bitter leaves among the lettuce stored there. Later, however, he found two potted foxglove plants in the back garden and on checking the browsing history of his computer discovered that someone had searched for information on

The leaves of *Digitalis purpurea*, a potentially deadly addition to a salad.

the toxicity of the foxglove. His wife denied buying the two plants and said that she had been researching toxic plants because she wanted to buy a plant as a gift for her sister but was keen to ensure the one she chose was not poisonous. She later pleaded guilty to reduced charges and was sentenced to four and a half years' imprisonment. Luckily the amount of *Digitalis* the victim had ingested was not sufficient to cause him great harm.

The foxglove has made a highly important contribution to the history of medicine and William Withering can be credited with carrying out the pioneering work to bring it into the realm of modern science. He established that it was active, developed a dosage schedule and described its side effects. These were, in fact, among the first clinical trials ever conducted. Medicine needs its heroes and Withering is unarguably one, having left a legacy second to none with his work on systematic botany, the heavy ore of Alston Moor and the foxglove. An important drug in the history of cardiology and a forerunner of the great advances that were to develop in the 20th century, digitalis is also dangerously toxic. A common garden plant, it is essential to ensure that gardeners and their children know of its poisonous nature as this powerful plant is certainly a healer but also a potential killer.

Rubiaceae.

Cephaelis Ipecacuanha Willd.

11 – Ipecacuanha *(Carapichea ipecacuanha)*: A Treatment for Amoebic Dysentery

The history of ipecacuanha is a fascinating one. Like quinine from *Cinchona*, and tubocurarine from *Chondrodendron* (see Chapters 13 and 7 respectively), ipecacuanha emerged from the forests of South America. From there it made its way to the capital cities of Europe, in particular Paris and Lisbon. Until the end of the 20th century, the root was used to make syrup of ipecac, a powerful medicine that was commonly used to induce vomiting. Syrup of ipecac was used especially after ingesting poison and as part of the treatment of what was then called 'the flux', now known as dysentery.

The word ipecacuanha derives from Tupi – a language spoken by the native Tupi people of Brazil – and can be roughly translated as 'low leaves vomit'. Ipecacuanha is defined in the French pharmacopoeia as follows: 'The root consists of the subterranean part of either *Cephaelis ipecacuanha* (Rubiaceae), known as Rio or Brazilian ipecac, or that of *Cephaelis acuminata* (the so-called Cartagena or Nicaraguan root)'.[1] Both of these species are now recognised under one species – *Carapichea ipecacuanha*.

The genus *Carapichea* is a group of five or six species that were separated from the genus *Cephaelis* in 2002. All are small perennial shrubs, growing to a height of 20–40 cm. Their leaves are arranged in opposite pairs up the stem and the stems terminate in a cluster of white flowers. The flowers are grouped into compact cymes (*cephaelis* means 'grouped at the head'). The roots consist of twisted fragments, like small beads on a necklace, ranging from 6 cm to 15 cm in diameter. When the shrubs were harvested, the roots were cut to size and dried slowly. Some of the roots were replanted to conserve the shrub, and a further harvest could be taken three to five years later. The plant was sold either as the dried root or in powder form.

The History of Ipecacuanha

How ipecacuanha reached Europe is something of a mystery. In the 17th and 18th centuries, there was a great deal of commercial traffic between South America and Portugal, Spain and, later, France. Merchants, priests and doctors would regularly make the journey

In Effigiem Nicholai Culpeper Equitis.
The shaddow of that Body heer you find,
Which serves but as a case to hold his mind,
His Intellectuall part be pleas'd to looke
In lively lines described in the Booke.   *Crose sculpsit*

The English botanist Nicholas Culpeper who described the use of ipecacuanha in his *Complete Herbal and English Physician* of 1652, from which this engraving is taken.

across the Atlantic. After the Jesuits discovered Peruvian bark (*Cinchona*), all the aforementioned groups were on the lookout for more powerful medicinal herbs. The first mention of ipecacuanha was in a 1648 collection of papers and notes by the German naturalist Georg Marggraf (1610–1644) and the Dutch naturalist Willem Pison (1611–1678), who travelled to Brazil in 1638 and whose findings were later published by Flemish geographer Jan Laet. Only a few years later, in 1653, the English botanist Nicholas Culpeper (1616–1654) described its use in his *Complete Herbal and English Physician*, in which he compared the plant to the herb orache (*Atriplex hortensis*). Subsequently a substantial amount of ipecacuanha was transported from South America into Europe, the first recorded occurrence of which was by a traveller called Legros, who in 1672 brought a large quantity of the root to Paris. It was used sporadically in France for the treatment of dysentery and ague (fever). For a time, supplies were very limited; however after 1680, when greater quantities became available, it was taken up by a number of physicians, most notably by Jean-Adrien Helvétius (1630–1709). At one stage Helvétius, for a time Chamberlain in the French court, used ipecacuanha root to treat a number of people in the royal household who were suffering from dysentery. One notable success was his treatment of the Dauphin (the heir to the throne), who made a complete recovery. Consequently, Helvétius enjoyed an enhanced reputation within royal circles, and King Louis XIV granted him a sole licence to sell ipecac root, although the government was later to buy back the licence and make the formula public.

When the root and powder became widely available in Europe in the 18th century, the indications for its use were studied intensively. It was established that in small doses, ipecac induced sweating and encouraged coughing. In larger doses, it caused vomiting and purging. At that time

disease was still regarded as an imbalance of the humours – the fluids that circulated through the body. If some of the 'bad' humours could be expelled by vomiting or purging, this was all to the good. As a result, ipecac became a popular supplement to traditional methods of restoring the balance of the humours, such as bleeding and cupping. Furthermore, poisoning was commonplace during this period in Paris, with the favoured substances including arsenic, antimony and henbane (see Chapter 3). Ipecac was a valuable antidote to poisoning if taken early enough.

As the 18th century ended, two problems surfaced with regard to the ipecac root: the nature of the plant source and the identity of the active principles contained therein. The first was solved by the introduction of the Linnaean binomial system for the identification and classification of plants. The second problem, which was the identification of the active substance, the alkaloid emetine, would prove much more difficult to solve and would await the advent of modern methods of chemistry in the 19th century.

Thomas Dover and Ipecacuanha

Thomas Dover (1660–1742) lived through a turbulent period in English history. Born in 1660 at the time of the restoration of Charles II, he survived the Glorious Revolution of 1688–1689 and lived on well into the Hanoverian period, dying in 1742 at the ripe old age of 82. He had started out as a sea captain and then privateer, at one point rescuing Alexander Selkirk when the latter was a castaway on the island of Juan Fernandez in the South Pacific, the inspiration for Daniel Defoe's *Robinson Crusoe*. He went on to be a distinguished, if controversial, physician. One of his medicinal preparations, Dover's powder, would survive for nearly 200 years. It was the standard treatment for gout until *Colchicum* arrived from the East (see Chapter 15). The major ingredients of Dover's powder were ipecacuanha, opium, saltpetre and cream of tartar. In small doses it was used to treat fever; in larger doses gout and dysentery. Dover often used potentially dangerous doses of the powder (60–80 g), and remarked acerbically that some apothecaries would advise patients 'to settle their affairs by making a last will and testament before venturing to take such a large dose'.[2]

The Healing Powers of Ipecacuanha and Emetine

During the period between 1850 and 1900, the 'golden age' of microbiology and pathology, many of the diagnostic dilemmas that had faced the physician and surgeon were resolved. As a result many of the empirical treatments for diseases, such as bleeding and purging, were abandoned and the scientific basis of medicine was established. Several important developments contributed to this explosion of knowledge, including the evolution of the compound microscope, the development of dyestuffs that would stain certain microbes and tissues and the discovery that bacteria could be cultivated in an artificial environment, using methods such as the Petri dish and the test tube.

As far as amoebic dysentery and its treatment with ipecacuanha was concerned, one of the first major developments came in 1875 when the Russian pathologist Fedor Lösch (1840–1903) examined the stool of a patient suffering from this complaint, and saw under the microscope a suspicious amoeba. Lösch called the presumed parasite *Amoeba coli*, although it was subsequently renamed *Entamoeba histolytica*. Some ten years later a similar *Entamoeba* was identified in pus from a patient's liver abscess. It was not until 1961 that Louis Diamond (1902–1999), an American paediatrician, was able to grow this amoeba in vitro (in an external environment rather

By permission of John Bell & Croyden www.johnbellcroyden.co.uk

An old box of ipecacuanha pills.

than within the living organism). During the same decade that *E. histolytica* was identified, it proved possible to identify the bacterial genera that were responsible for other forms of dysentery. These proved to be largely *Salmonella* or *Shigella* species and it transpired that neither the pure emetine alkaloid nor the complex mixture obtained from ipecac root had any effect on these bacterial organisms and were thus ineffective at treating bacterial dysentery.

In the 20th century, when the pure alkaloid emetine became generally available, large-scale trials were undertaken by scientists including Sir Leonard Rogers (1868–1962), a London-based professor of tropical medicine. There was no doubt that emetine was extremely effective in eradicating the amoebae, but there were considerable practical difficulties in its use. The patient had to be kept on bed rest for the duration of treatment, the drug was best given by injection and close observation had to be maintained to detect potentially fatal cardiovascular complications, including hypotension and tachycardia (a fast or irregular heart rate). If either of these two problems occurred, treatment had to be stopped immediately. In spite of these rigorous precautions, there were nonetheless occasional cases of sudden death. As a result, from 1950

Emetine

Modern chemical knowledge began to emerge as a specific discipline in the latter part of the 18th century. There were several important developments in this period and, at the end of the Napoleonic Wars (1803–1815), a great chemical enterprise became concentrated in Paris, at both the University and the School of

Emetine

Cephaeline methyl ether

$C_{29}H_{40}N_2O_4$

Pharmacy. The three main protagonists in this famous school were François Magendie (1783–1855), Pierre-Joseph Pelletier (1788–1842) and Joseph-Bienaimé Caventou (1795–1887) (facing page, left to right). This brilliant group, in a sustained period of excellent work, isolated a number of alkaloids: emetine, brucine, strychnine and quinine. They also extracted and named the important plant pigment chlorophyll, the basis of photosynthesis. Moreover, together with Mathieu-Joseph Bonaventure Orfila (1787–1853), often known as the founder of modern toxicology, they studied the pathological effects of these alkaloids in animals.

The main alkaloids found in the root of ipecac are emetine and cephaeline. Both alkaloids are complex molecules, and the details of their structure were not established until the 20th century. Emetine is obtained either by direct extraction of ipecac root or by methylation (the addition of a methyl CH3 group) to cephaeline, which is also obtained from the plant.

onwards, alternative treatments were sought that would prove to be effective by mouth and be free from potentially lethal cardiac effects. As soon as these came into use, emetine was rarely, if ever, used.

The powdered root of ipecac was also made into a syrup that until the late 20th century was commonly used to induce vomiting in cases of accidental or deliberate poisoning. The dried root contains many compounds other than emetine and cephaeline, but it was thought that these small amounts of other compounds in the root did not make any significant contribution to its properties in precipitating vomiting. The powder had a dual-action effect on the body: directly irritating the stomach and upper gut

and, after absorption into the bloodstream, acting on the trigger zone in the lower part of the brain. Generally speaking, ipecac root was thought to be an effective and safe way to induce vomiting. In Britain it was generally used only in accident and emergency departments, while in the United States and Australia it was often kept in the home as a first-aid measure in cases of accidental poisoning. Although it largely had a good safety record, ipecac occasionally produced severe complications, including ruptures of the oesophagus and stomach, sometimes with fatal results.

As time went on, however, doubts arose as to the extent to which vomiting actually

(left to right) François Magendie, Pierre-Joseph Pelletier and Joseph-Bienaimé Caventou, the men who first isolated emetine.

It has many actions, both biochemical (on tissue and cells) and pharmacological (on whole animals). In therapeutic doses, emetine also has a direct lethal action on the tissue and cells of *Entamoeba histolytica*, the causative protozoan of amoebic dysentery. Pure emetine proved to be a toxic drug when used clinically, as its therapeutic ratio (the difference between its therapeutic dose and its toxic dose) is narrow. Adverse reactions could affect the gastrointestinal tract (vomiting and diarrhoea), the nervous system (inflammation of the peripheral nerves) and the heart (arrhythmia, hypotension and sudden death).

caused significant amounts of poison to be removed from the body. Another concern was that ipecac could not be combined with activated charcoal, the preferred treatment, as it could induce vomiting of the absorbent charcoal, reducing its effect. This resulted in a consensus view in the 1990s that the use of ipecac should be abandoned and safer, more effective treatments used instead. In addition, ipecacuanha was used in many cases by those suffering from anorexia nervosa and bulimia nervosa in order to deliberately initiate vomiting. As it was possible to buy the drug over the counter until the 1980s, people with these conditions would often use it to make themselves sick after eating. This sadly could, and often did, prove fatal.

Compared with quinine, which has saved the lives of millions of malaria sufferers, it would appear that ipecacuanha is but a minor player in medicine. Nevertheless, emetine was the first effective and relatively safe emetic. More importantly, perhaps, it was the first efficient amoebicide and, for around a century, the only one available. It also enabled physicians to make the important distinction between amoebic and bacillary dysentery, a key distinction in the history of both parasitology and bacteriology.

Compositae.

Artemisia Absinthium L.

WM. n.d.Nat.

12 – The Wormwoods (*Artemisia annua* and *absinthium*): A Bittersweet Experience

This chapter differs from its predecessors in that it describes two species from one genus, thus demonstrating the differing nature of plant chemical toxins. *Artemisia annua* (sweet wormwood), known to Chinese herbal practitioners for several millennia but introduced into Western allopathic medicine only in the 1980s, has proved one of the most successful anti-malarials of modern times. The plant has survived the rigours of modern scientific analysis and borne out its ancient reputation as a weapon against this deadly disease. In contrast, *Artemisia absinthium* (bitter wormwood) began its story as a medicine used to treat intestinal worms, but became infamous in its reincarnation as a component of the drink absinthe. According to its detractors, the 'green fairy' was responsible for many of the social ills of the 19th century.

The genus *Artemisia* is a member of the daisy family Asteraceae (also called Compositae) and comprises more than 300 species of annual, biennial and perennial herbs and shrubs, known for their essential oils. The plants have pinnate, divided, silky, hairy leaves and these are often grey to white in colour. The tiny flowers are arranged in pendant daisy-like heads but with no rays. *Artemisia* species grow in temperate climates, usually in rather dry habitats. It is an important genus and, apart from *A. annua* and *A. absinthium*, includes species such as *A. dracunculus*, commonly known as tarragon and widely used in cooking, *A. vulgaris* (mugwort) and *A. pontica* (Roman wormwood). Mugwort is a venerable herb with a long history of treating women's ailments. A good description of this herb was given by the Greek physician Dioscorides (c. AD 40–90) when he claimed that it gave succour to women in labour. *A. annua* is a very vigorous, bright-green annual, growing to over 2 m in the right conditions, while *A. absinthum* is shorter in stature, perennial and slightly woody at the base with leaves covered in a silvery down. The latter is common in gardens as a herbaceous border plant. The genus was named after the Greek goddess Artemis. She is chiefly associated with the wildlife of the earth, human fertility, reproduction and childbirth and often appeared as a huntress with a deer and a quiver of arrows (her Roman equivalent is Diana).

The goddess Artemis as illustrated in Linnaeus' *Fauna Svecica* of 1746, and after whom the genus is named. The multi-breasted Artemis is the goddess of, amongst other things, childbirth and fertility.

Artemisinin

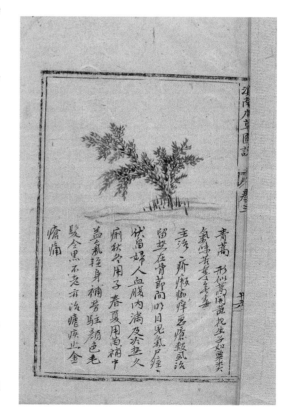

$$C_{15}H_{22}O_5$$

Artemisinin and Alpha-thujone

The structure of the active compound artemesinin (from *Artemisia annua*) and alpha-thujone (from *Artemisia absinthium*) show no chemical relationship to each other. The name thujone is derived from the genus *Thuja*, which is applied to two North American conifer trees, *Thuja occidentalis* and *Thuja plicata*, known respectively as the western white cedar and the western red cedar. Both these trees produce alpha-thujone, as their generic name would suggest. They are also an important source of medicinal fragrant oils and belong to the family Cupressaceae (the cypresses). Another plant unrelated to *A. absinthium* which produces alpha-thujone is the tansy (*Tanacetum vulgare*). This is an aromatic perennial and also belongs to the family Asteraceae (or Compositae). It has been used in the past as a medicinal herb and as a tonic tea. The fact that the three different genera *Thuja*, *Artemisia* and *Tanacetum* can all produce alpha-thujone is an example of an interesting, although not especially uncommon, phenomenon. It seems to be a case of convergent evolution in order to produce a compound that can effectively deter animals, birds and insects from their predation.

A painting of sweet wormwood from the *Illustrated Yunnan Pharmacopoeia* compiled by the Ming writer Lan Mao in the 14th–15th century. The book provides a record of the plants and other substances commonly used for medicinal purposes in Yunnan in the Ming period.

Qinghao: The Healer

The Chinese Emperor Shennong (born c. 2800 BC), known as the Divine Farmer, described the properties and uses of hundreds of medicinal herbs, information that was later set down by an anonymous scribe in a work named *Shennong Bencao Jing* (*The Divine Farmer's Herb Root Classic*) (see Chapter 9). Among the herbs he described was *Artemisia annua*, known in Chinese medicine as *qinghao*, which was said to be effective in the treatment of fever. It should be remembered that in ancient times fever was considered as a specific disease in its own right and not simply a symptom of another more specific ailment. The Divine Farmer's successor Huangdi, the Yellow Emperor (c. 2696–2598 BC), and his close associates developed techniques to diagnose and treat disease, later recorded in a work entitled *Huangdi Neijing* (*The Yellow Emperor's Inner Classic*). This work contains what is thought to be the first-ever written description of malaria.

A close-up of an *Anopheles gambiae* female mosquito biting into human skin. *Anopheles* mosquitoes transmit malaria. The parasite responsible for malaria (*Plasmodium*) is carried in the female mosquito's saliva.

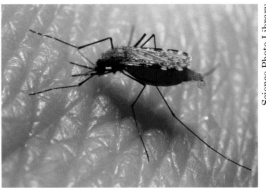

Malaria has been common in south-west China for millennia, where it is known as *nue ji* (literally 'wet weather disease' or 'monsoon disease'). In this area of China it is both endemic and, in the rainy season, epidemic. For centuries it was claimed that several different herbs were an effective treatment. The first to gain scientific validation was qinghao. Specific mention of this herb occurs with its description in *Wushi'er Bingfang* (*Recipes for 52 Kinds of Diseases*), a medical text found in 1973 in the Han dynasty tomb at Mawangdui, which had been sealed in 168 BC. The text itself is thought to have been written around 50 years before that. The herb was further described in *Zhouhou Jiuzufang* (*Handbook of Prescriptions for Emergencies*), written by the philosopher and alchemist Ge Hong (AD 283–343) in around AD 340. Despite

these written references to *Artemisia annua* occurring over several centuries, the key questions remained unanswered until modern times: what is the active compound in this plant and does it kill *Plasmodium*, the single-celled parasite that causes malaria?

Traditional Chinese herbal remedies are often mixtures based upon the principles of yin and yang: that is, the so-called 'active' agent is balanced by other agents that will counteract the adverse effects of the former. For example, a so-called 'hot' drug will be balanced by a 'cold' drug, or a 'wet' one by a 'drying' compound. This makes identification of the active principle of these mixtures very difficult. In 1967, the Chinese government, led by Mao Zedong, set up 'Project 523', a long-term systematic examination of all the indigenous plants contained in their many traditional herbal remedies. The aim was to find an effective treatment for malaria, which had become resistant to chloroquine, a drug used in its prevention and treatment since the 1940s. This was at the request of their ally North Vietnam, whose military were in dire need of anti-malarial drugs. The project was a task of undeniable magnitude, involving several hundred scientists and between 3,000 and 5,000 herbs. The occurrence of multiple combinations of herbs was a significant problem, making the identification of the 'active' herb nigh on impossible.

A watercolour of Shennong at the mouth of a cave dressed in clothing made from leaves. Emperor Shennong described the properties of hundreds of medicinal herbs.

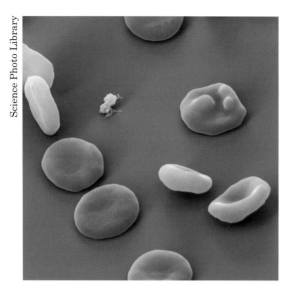

Science Photo Library

An SEM of a red blood cell infected with *Plasmodium falciparum* protozoa. These protozoa (yellow) cause malaria. The red blood cell on the right shows orange bulges caused by the *Plasmodium* invasion.

An extract made from the dried leaves of *Artemisia annua* established that the preparation was highly active against malaria. Initial attempts to isolate the active principle from the plant failed, but in 1971 success was achieved when Tu Youyou (1930–), a scientist working on Project 523, located it in the plant's leaves. It was named artemisinin (*qinghaosu* in Chinese). Artemisinin was found to cure mice infected with *Plasmodium berghei* (a parasite causing malaria in rodents). The scientific advance remained unknown to the rest of the world until the late 1970s, and even for years after that there was a reluctance on the part of the Chinese government to allow access to any information about the drug for economic and military reasons.

The first definitive trials of artemisinin were carried out in 1979. Altogether 2,099 patients were treated and all were cured. Additionally, 143 patients with chloroquine-resistant falciparum malaria (a severe form of malaria caused by the *Plasmodium falciparum* parasite) were treated, as well as 141 people suffering from cerebral malaria (a type affecting the brain). These patients, too, had good outcomes. Many other trials were carried out in China and South-East Asia, confirming this first groundbreaking Chinese study. The most striking results were seen in the treatment of cerebral malaria, where 'cure' rates of up to 90 per cent were achieved.

Unfortunately, a significant problem emerged in the course of the artemisinin trials. Up to 10 per cent of the patients studied suffered a relapse. However, studies in Thailand showed that this 'failure' rate could be reduced to 2 to 5 per cent if artemisinin were combined with mefloquine, which kills the parasite by a different mechanism; this would also have the effect of delaying the patient's resistance to mefloquine. A further benefit

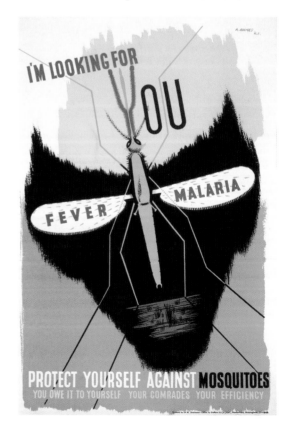

I'M LOOKING FOR YOU

FEVER   MALARIA

PROTECT YOURSELF AGAINST MOSQUITOES
YOU OWE IT TO YOURSELF   YOUR COMRADES   YOUR EFFICIENCY

A World War II poster warning troops against the dangers of malaria, produced in 1941 by HM Stationery Office.

was that these drugs in combination would kill the sexual forms of the parasite, thus delaying or preventing transmission of the malarial infection. In 2006, the World Health Organisation pronounced that artemisinin should not be given alone, as resistance to the drug had now begun to develop in the *Plasmodium* parasite. It advised that appropriate steps, such as the use of combination therapy, should now be taken. Since then, artemisinin has been prescribed in combination with other anti-malarial drugs. Further combinations of drugs are constantly under investigation with the aim of increasing the cure rate in malaria and preventing the development of resistance in the parasite.

Bitter Wormwood: A Deadly Cousin

In the same way as the Chinese were aware of the medical applications of *Artemisia annua* several millennia ago, so too have the therapeutic benefits of another perennial herb of the same genus been known for thousands of years. This is its cousin *A. absinthium*, used widely as a vermifuge (a treatment to kill intestinal worms). It is mentioned by the Prophet Jeremiah in the Old Testament ('Behold, I will feed them with wormwood, and make them drink the water of gall')[1] as being a particularly bitter herb, given to sinners as punishment. Believed to be indigenous to some parts of the Eastern Mediterranean, the herb would probably have remained of little significance without the developments in the French alcohol industry in the 19th century.

It was discovered that if *A. absinthium* (or *A. maritima* or *A. pontica*) was distilled with alcohol together with anise (*Pimpinella anisum*), fennel (*Foeniculum vulgare*) and other herbs, it produced a beautiful green liquid which came to be known as *la fée verte* (the green fairy). Its alcohol content was about 75 per cent, a factor which contributed

A New Angle for the Pentagon

Since fighting in the Pacific in World War II, military leaders in the United States have been painfully aware of the human cost of fighting in this theatre of action. Casualties included not only combat deaths and disability but also those due to malaria, typhus and arboviruses (carried by mosquitoes and ticks). According to the terms of a treaty between the United States and Taiwan signed in 1955, if China attacked Taiwan, then the United States would have to come to the latter's rescue. The Pentagon realised that the Chinese had acquired qinghaosu to use as a treatment for malaria and would therefore have a definite military advantage in any land war in Asia. This was particularly important as the *Plasmodium* parasite had become widely resistant to chloroquine. The military leaders asked the Walter Reed Army Institute, a major military institution located in Washington DC, whether qinghaosu could be identified and, if so, if the plant from which it was derived grew anywhere in the United States. The answer, in fact, lay right on their own doorstep. Amongst a number of areas investigated was the Potomac River, as it flows through Maryland into Washington and down to the sea. *Artemisia annua* was located in several sites along the lower part of the river and down into the Potomac basin. Extracts of the herb were made and artemisinin recovered. It later turned out that *A. annua* was very well known to US botanists, having been introduced from the Middle East and Asia in the 19th century. The early settlers had used it as a preservative and flavouring and called it 'sweet Annie'. The Pentagon panic was over.

α-Thujone

(—)-Isothujone

$C_{10}H_{16}O$

greatly to the side effects caused by drinking absinthe regularly to excess.

Absinthe was first made in 1792 by a French doctor living in Switzerland, Pierre Ordinaire (1741–1821), who was looking to

A late-19th-century label design for Absinthe Suisse, the alcoholic drink made using a variety of plants, including *Artemisia absinthium*.

supply the extract of the plant, with its known medicinal properties, in a form that was easy to ingest. He eventually sold the secret formula to Henri-Louis Pernod (1776–1851) who first manufactured small quantities in Switzerland but in 1805 set up a distillery in France for the mass production of the drink. Its popularity increased throughout the 1800s, helped largely by the fact that the French army used it extensively as an anti-malarial in their North African campaigns. On their return, they helped spread its popularity, making it the favoured beverage of the 19th century in France, across all social classes but particularly among the bohemian community of writers and artists in Paris. Oscar Wilde, Vincent van Gogh, Pablo Picasso, Ernest Hemingway and Charles Baudelaire were among its noted consumers, with literature and art of the time often executed under its influence.

In small amounts absinthe stimulated the mind, but excessive use was said to cause

QUALITÉ   SUPÉRIEUR

ABSINTHE
SUISSE

DUPRÉ   N° 71   PARIS

A poster from 1910 which shows the victory of medicine and organised religion over the freedom of the individual to consume absinthe. The green fairy lies dead at the feet of the grinning man with his bible and medical cross as he points to the date when the consumption of absinthe was banned in Switzerland.

LA FIN DE LA «FÉE VERTE»
(Suppression de l'Absinthe en Suisse)

Adieu, chère liberté d'Industrie
Offert par la Maison Girbou et Trachlin à Plainont

absinthism, a specific type of alcoholism that made drinkers lethargic and feeble, mentally unstable and often tormented by hallucinations or prone to epileptic fits. Critics of the beverage claimed that it led to social unrest, criminality, violence and insanity. A notorious case is that of the Swiss farmer Jean Lanfray (1873–1906), a noted alcoholic and absinthe drinker. At the end of a day of heavy drinking, during which he had imbibed wine, cognac, liqueurs and two glasses of absinthe, he had an argument with his wife and shot her and his two daughters dead. Convicted of murder, he was sent to a mental institution for life, having been diagnosed as suffering from madness caused solely by the absinthe he had drunk. Whether this is the case is open to question, as it was all too easy for prohibitionists to conveniently ignore the fact that he had spent all day drinking a variety of alcoholic beverages.

That said, the toxic substance contained in absinthe, alpha-thujone, is damaging to all nervous tissue including the higher functions of the brain, and can cause amnesia, dementia, convulsions and hallucinations. By 1913, the French were consuming around 36 million litres of the drink every year and the number of crimes committed by its drinkers was rising alarmingly, including murder while under the influence of paranoid delusions and hallucinations. As a consequence of the Lanfray case, in 1913 Switzerland banned the manufacture of absinthe if it contained wormwood and France followed suit in 1915. In the 1990s there were attempts to make absinthe fashionable once more, especially in countries where it had never been formally banned, such as the United Kingdom. The ban was officially lifted in Switzerland in 2000 and in France in 2011.

The genus *Artemisia* contains a number of species which resemble each other closely in appearance but contain chemical compounds which are unrelated in their structure. As a result these different compounds have widely different therapeutic and toxic actions. *A. absinthium* would probably have been confined to history in the 19th century when newer, more effective vermifuges appeared. The development of the green liquor saved it from obscurity, taking it down the path of infamy instead. In contrast, *A. annua* had lurked in the shadowland of Chinese herbal medicine for centuries but then emerged in the 1980s to join quinine as one of the cornerstones of anti-malarial therapy. This genus has without a doubt given us both bitter and sweet.

Rubiaceae.

Cinchona officinalis Hook. fil.

13 – Peruvian Bark *(Cinchona officinalis)*: The First Effective Treatment for Malaria

One of the most compelling sagas in the history of medicine and therapeutics is that of the discovery of Peruvian bark (*Cinchona*) and the pharmacologically active substance derived from it, quinine. It involves exploration, exploitation and secrecy, spans the globe from South America to the Dutch East Indies and, in the 19th century, came to reflect the struggles of the major European powers for domination, territory and profit.

The work of the French botanist Hugh Algernon Weddell (1819–1877) in the 19th century showed that the genus *Cinchona* is a complex one. A member of the Rubiaceae family, the genus comprises 40 species. In their natural habitat the trees grow up to 20 m in height. The leaves are decussate (with opposite pairs at 90° to neighbouring pairs) and often have a pinkish stalk and midrib. The flowers are regular, white or pink, tubular and appear in groups of five. The trees are indigenous to the eastern slopes of the Andes from Colombia in the north through Ecuador to Peru in the south. They grow at altitudes between 1,500 and 3,000 m, from 10° north of the Equator to 20° south, in areas with substantial rainfall and relatively constant temperature. Many hybrids and cultivars are known.

The Cardinal's Bark

The first definite written account of the medicinal properties of the bark of the fever tree appears to be that by Antonio de la Calancha (1584–1684), an Augustinian missionary and anthropologist who in 1633 wrote an account of a tree growing in Loja, Peru, the bark of which, when made into a powder, cured tertian fevers (recurring every third day). How the bark made its way to Europe is not known for sure, but it seems likely that Jesuit priests, who travelled widely throughout South America doing missionary work, introduced it to Spain and Italy.

A Spanish Jesuit priest living in Rome, Cardinal Juan de Lugo (1583–1660), obtained a quantity of Peruvian bark and, impressed by his preliminary trials of its efficacy, purchased a large amount of it at his own expense. A contemporary reported that de Lugo gave doses to the poor for free, asking only that they did not resell it and that they reported back to him whether or not it had worked. Word of its success as a treatment for fever spread, and so church couriers took the bark further afield in Italy and onwards to

A copy of the fresco in the Ospedale di Santo Spirito, an ancient hospital in Rome, which shows Cardinal de Lugo dispensing *Cinchona*.

The mosquito *Anopheles atroparvus* indigenous to Britain and capable of carrying the *Plasmodium vivax* parasite which causes tertian malaria. This historic drawing is an example of the male of the species.

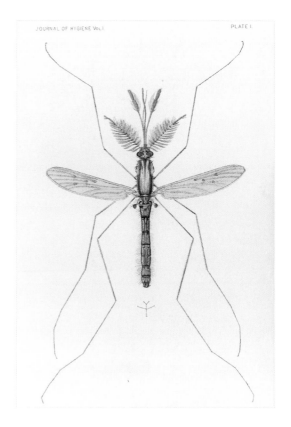

JOURNAL OF HYGIENE Vol.I   PLATE I.

other parts of Europe, including Germany and Great Britain, where it was known as Jesuit's bark. In return Cardinal de Lugo received a large collection of testimonial letters and the plant also became known as *pulvis cardinalis* (cardinal's powder) or *pulvis de Lugo*.

The English Connection

The bark probably arrived in England via Belgium or Holland. The first definite mention of its use there was by an apothecary in Northampton in 1656, who reported that he had cured a pregnant woman of a quartan fever (recurring every four days) by giving her small doses of the bark. Unfortunately, at about the same time, a London alderman died after taking what appears to have been an overdose of the medication. It fell to an apothecary's apprentice, Robert Talbor (1642–1681), to confirm the importance of administering the correct dose of the bark and so make its use more widespread. Talbor was born in the cathedral city of Ely in the Fens in 1642. The Fens were a low-lying swampy area that had not yet been drained, and as a

An etching of Ely Cathedral in the home town of Robert Talbor. The position of the cathedral city on the Fens made its occupants susceptible to malaria, a problem Talbor was determined to solve.

result the inhabitants were subject to severe tertian and quartan fevers which caused a great deal of misery and sometimes proved fatal. Talbor resolved to tackle this problem and the opportunity arose when he was apprenticed as a trainee apothecary to a Mr Dent in Cambridge.

During his apprenticeship he learnt of the existence of Jesuit's bark and resolved to carry out further work on the substance. He left his apprenticeship, moved to a marshy malarious area of Essex and began a long series of experiments on the bark. He kept his experiments and results to himself as he intended to reap some pecuniary advantage. During the course of the 1660s he was able to develop a formulation of the bark which proved very successful in curing the 'Essex ague', probably caused either by *Plasmodium malariae* or by *P. viva*, transmitted by the mosquito *Anopheles atroparvus*.

Charles II came to know of Talbor's success in treating the ague and appointed him King's Physician in Ordinary in 1672, much to the annoyance of the medical establishment. He was subsequently knighted in 1678. With his royal endorsement, he decided in 1672 to move to London, where he established himself as a fever specialist. Talbot's secret, and the basis of the English remedy, seems to have been relatively simple: he gave larger doses of Peruvian bark at more frequent intervals, and did not bleed or purge his patients. Moreover, he administered the bark immediately after a shivering fit and then used smaller doses to prevent relapse. His only gesture to the then-prevalent polypharmacy (the use of multiple types of medication at the same time) was to infuse the bark in white wine and to add sweet herbs in an attempt to disguise the extremely bitter taste. In 1679, Charles II asked Talbor to go to France to attempt to cure the Dauphin of a recurring ague. This endeavour proved successful and Louis XIV, as a gesture of gratitude, made Talbor a Chevalier of France and bought the secret

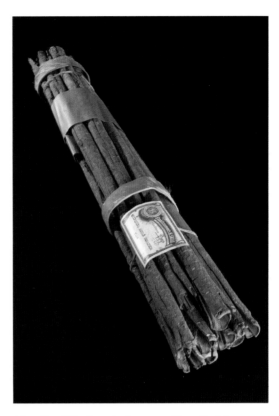

A bundle of *Cinchona* bark prepared by a Parisian pharmacist for his shop in 1930–1931.

of the English remedy from him for 2,000 louis d'or, then a considerable sum of money. Talbor stipulated that the remedy should remain secret until his death, which occurred in 1681. In 1682, the King of France published *Le remède anglais pour la guérison des fièvres*. Shortly afterwards an English version was published with the subtitle 'Talbor's wonderful secret for curing agues and fevers'. The success of these two books sent the price of the bark shooting up across Europe.

Barking up the Wrong Tree

In many ways the late 17th century was still a pre-scientific age. Little systematic botany existed before Carl Linnaeus's magisterial work in taxonomy, and chemistry was still dominated by the alchemists. With the marked rise in the price of Peruvian bark across Europe, cheating was common. Other bitter substances were used

LIGNUM FEBRIUM.

The Lignum febrium, tree of fevers, as illustrated in Francesco Torti's 1712 book *Therapeutice Specialis ad Febres Periodicas Perniciosas*.

bark, whereas denuded, leafless branches represented fevers resistant to the medication. This work was to pave the way for the idea of the therapeutic trial for medicinal compounds.

The Search for the Tree

With the increased demand for the bark, its rising price and the confusion over the identity of the tree from which the bark was derived, it now became essential to locate the tree in its native habitat. In 1735, the French government sent an expedition to South America, led by the explorer Charles Marie de la Condamine (1701–1774). One objective was to find the fever tree. Condamine succeeded in doing this near Loja in Peru. In 1738, Condamine published his monograph *Sur l'arbre du Quinquina* which contained the first clear and detailed illustration of the fever tree. On the basis of this illustration, Carl Linnaeus, in 1742, included this plant in his *Genera plantarum* under the title *Cinchona*, named after the Countess of Chinchón, wife of the Viceroy of Peru, said to have been treated for fever by Peruvian bark. It should have been called *Chinchona* but Linnaeus's mistake

as substitutes, such as cherry bark or aloes steeped in water. Bark was also sold that had been extracted once and had thereby lost almost its entire therapeutic activity. To make matters worse, it was impossible to tell from inspecting the bark just how much of the active principle it contained. No assay, biological or chemical, was available at this time and so all sorts of bark were in circulation, some genuine, some not.

Other problems developed with the clinical use of the bark; fever was regarded as a specific disease, not as a symptom of many different diseases. This confusion began to be clarified by the Italian physician Francesco Torti (1658–1741), who realised that there were many different kinds of fevers and that some responded to Peruvian bark and some did not. In his 1712 book *Therapeutice Specialis ad Febres Periodicas Perniciosas*, he showed an illustration of a tree of fevers. Branches of the tree covered with bark represented fevers curable by Peruvian

A portrait of Charles Marie de la Condamine, the French explorer who was sent in search of the fever tree and subsequently published the first detailed description of it.

An oil painting showing the isolation of quinine by Pelletier and Caventou in 1820.

has never been corrected in spite of prolonged discussion at several international conferences.

Following the French expedition, trade in the bark once again developed rapidly, with Loja at its centre. In the latter part of the 19th century the situation became rather chaotic. In the early days, the Jesuits had taught the *cascarilleros* (bark cutters) to plant five cuttings in the form of a cross for every *Cinchona* that was felled. This injunction was now sadly forgotten as trees were torn down without being replaced. The bark was often adulterated with that of other trees and widespread smuggling took place to try to outwit the Spanish authorities. The Spanish government set up a monopoly in an attempt to improve the quality, yield and processing methods for the bark. This was particularly successful in controlling supplies, further helped by the discovery of forests in Colombia, Bolivia and Ecuador. Nevertheless, supply of the bark could barely match demand and was further threatened by wars and revolutions.

The Isolation of Quinine

In the late 18th and early 19th centuries a number of chemists and pharmacists attempted to discover the active principle of Peruvian bark. Some success was achieved in extracting an active substance from the bark but it was French chemists Pierre-Joseph Pelletier (1788–1842) and Joseph-Bienaimé Caventou (1795–1887) who, in 1820, found success. Building on an initial successful extraction they went on to isolate two active alkaloids, quinine and cinchonine. Following this important breakthrough, several physicians demonstrated that the pure alkaloid quinine was very effective in treating tertian and quartan fevers and that the resinous and woody residues remaining after the extraction of the alkaloid were essentially inactive. As early as 1821, Pelletier and others began to manufacture quinine and, as the salt quinine sulphate, it rapidly became known and used worldwide. Pelletier and Caventou did not patent their

process but in a humanitarian gesture allowed it to be produced everywhere without demanding any licensing fees, and this helped greatly in its widespread use throughout the world.

From 1820 onwards, and for more than the next 100 years, determined attempts were made to synthesise quinine. The problem resisted all efforts until 1944, when at Harvard University, Robert Woodward (1917–1979) and William Doering (1917–2011) succeeded in doing so. However, the process was lengthy, complicated and expensive, and, as a result, it did not become a commercial threat to extraction of the alkaloid from the bark of natural *Cinchona*.

The Scramble for Quinine

The French, British and Dutch governments all had colonies in South-East Asia, India and Africa, areas plagued with recurrent fevers. It was thought that if *Cinchona* trees or their seeds could be taken from South America and established elsewhere, it would help the imperial powers to exploit their colonies and would have the added benefit of establishing the tree outside the new South American republics, where the political situation was volatile. The first partial success was achieved by Hugh Algernon Weddell. A noted authority on the classification of the *Cinchona* genus, he returned to his homeland of France in 1849 carrying seeds of *Cinchona calisaya*. These were successfully germinated

A plantation of *Cinchona* in the Nilgiri Hills, Tamil Nadu State, India. The image shows the governor of Madras planting the first tree of a new plantation.

and the seeds used to grow a young tree which was then sent to Java, where it flourished. This is believed to be the first *Cinchona* tree to have been cultivated outside South America.

Britain also succeeded in the effort to establish the trees elsewhere, at least for a time, mostly thanks to the work of Clements Markham (1830–1916), a government clerk based in London. In 1859, he was commissioned to collect young trees and seeds from the eastern Andes and acclimatise them to India and Ceylon. The first batches of plants sent from Peru in 1860 all died, but further batches sent in 1861, when transferred to the Nilgiri Hills near Madras, found conditions similar to those of the eastern Andes. By 1866, these plantations were able to supply London with adequate amounts of bark. Unfortunately many of the trees succumbed to attack by insects, and the yield of quinine from the bark of those varieties could not compete with *Cinchona ledgeriana*. Eventually the Indian growers would switch production from *Cinchona* to tea.

The forgotten man of this saga is the alpaca farmer Charles Ledger (1818–1905). He managed to get some seeds out of Bolivia, despite it being prohibited to do so. The British government showed little interest in Ledger's findings but the Dutch authorities bought one pound of the seeds and planted them in Java, where they went on

to form the basis of the world's present supply. Through careful cultivation and experimentation in Java the yield from the bark of *Cinchona ledgeriana*, named in Ledger's honour, was doubled when compared with the wild variety in Peru and Bolivia. In 1942, the Japanese captured Java and the *Cinchona* fields were no longer available to the Allies. This led to a worldwide shortage of quinine and to urgent production of synthetic anti-malarials such as mepacrine and chloroquine. The search for natural plant products active against malaria was effectively abandoned.

The Malarial Parasite Revealed

By the middle of the 19th century it was clear that quinine was an effective remedy against malarial fever but, as Torti had suggested, it was inactive as a treatment for other agues. Then physicians started to suggest that quinine might act by killing a parasitic or invasive living organism, such as a fungus or bacterium. In 1880 came a breakthrough. Charles Louis

A 1909 cartoon of Charles Louis Alphonse Laveran slaying mosquitos.

Professor LAVERAN

Quinine

When the parasites had been identified (together with their asexual and sexual forms) their lifecycle and the action of quinine upon these phases could be established. Quinine appears to have no action against the sporozoites (the immature forms of the parasites) and is virtually inactive against the gametocytes (the sexual forms). The mechanism of action seems to be rapid uptake into the blood cells followed by inhibition of protein synthesis in the parasite.

Quinine still has a place in modern treatment of malaria where it is used in severe and complicated malignant tertian malaria, where invasion of the brain (cerebral malaria) or massive breakdown of the red cells (blackwater fever) occurs. Quinine is also used as a bitter agent in drinks and other flavourings, and as a source of quinidine, the stereoisomer of quinine, a drug used to treat irregular heart rhythms.

Quinine

$C_{20}H_{24}N_2O_2$

Alphonse Laveran (1845–1922), a French surgeon working in the military hospital at Constantine in Algeria, started to look under the microscope at fresh blood smears from patients with 'malaria'. At the periphery of the smears he noticed some mobile elements. He thought that they resembled protozoa and observed that from time to time they showed extremely motile external appendages, called flagellae. He called his new-found organism *Oscillarina malariae* after the active flagellae and the association with malaria. A modern interpretation of his observations would say that he was observing the sexual forms of *Plasmodium falciparum*, the cause of malignant tertian malaria. Much further work by many investigators would establish the different forms of *Plasmodia* (as the parasites came to be called) and their lifecycle in the *Anopheles* mosquito.

Cinchonism

Quinine, if taken on a chronic basis for the prevention of malaria, can give rise to an unusual constellation of symptoms known as cinchonism. These include tinnitus (ringing in the ears), amaurosis (blurred vision) and paraesthesiae (pins and needles). The drug must be stopped completely, otherwise the syndrome may cause blindness or deafness due to constriction of the central artery to the retina or cochlea, or may even prove fatal. Most symptoms, however, are reversible and will disappear once the patient has stopped taking the drug. Once also a common treatment for cramp, quinine has now been totally replaced by the common tranquilliser diazepam, which is less dangerous for vital brain structures.

It is now almost 400 years since the Jesuits in Peru identified the bark of the *Cinchona* as being an effective cure for fever. At first there was the bark but no tree; then the tree but no compound; then the substance quinine but no chemical structure or effective synthesis. Finally the parasite *Plasmodium* was identified, the structure of quinine determined and the facts fitted together to form a convincing and coherent picture. It is a story involving bravery, generosity, greed, exploitation and the colonial ambitions of the great European powers. As we sip our gin and tonic we should reflect on the bark collectors, the Jesuits and de Lugo, Condamine, Pelletier and Caventou, Ledger and Laveran, and raise our glass to all who served in the quest for quinine.

XVII, 9.   11. Taxineae.

22. Taxus baccata L. Eibe.

14 – The European Yew (*Taxus baccata*): The Source of Powerful Anti-cancer Agents

The yew has always held a special place in both medicine and mythology. It is recognised in folklore and religion as a symbol of death and, at the same time, an emblem of eternal life. This duality has extended with the modern era of science, where the yew has shown its paradoxical nature as both a healer and a killer. The anti-cancer properties of compounds produced from its bark have proved powerful in the efforts to fight the disease, but it still remains one of the more widely known plants used in suicide attempts and is also responsible for some cases of accidental poisoning.

There have been many arguments between learned authorities about speciation in the genus *Taxus*. Some argue that there is only one species (*T. baccata*) and that this varies from place to place in leaf form and colour, depending on climate, day length and so on. Others maintain that there are distinct species which include *T. canadensis* (found in north-east America), *T. brevifolia* (the Pacific coast), *T. cuspidata* (Japan) and *T. wallichiana* (Himalayas). Many cultivated varieties have arisen by chance, such as one from County Fermanagh, Northern Ireland, *T. baccata* 'Fastigiata' (the Irish yew) which is more upright in habit than the typical wild species. Yews are dioecious, that is with separate male and female plants. The female cones of the yew consist of a pair of naked ovules surrounded by overlapping scales. In contrast, male cones are borne in small showers on the underside of the twigs. The needles are flat, dark green and softly pointed, with a faint midrib. In February and March the males produce clouds of yellow pollen which scatter to the winds. When fertilised the ovule becomes a seed, surrounded by a fleshy, bright-red aril. This berry-like structure attracts birds that act as dispersers for the plant. The Florida yew, Mexican yew and Pacific yew are all rare species listed as threatened or endangered. At the Royal Botanic Garden Edinburgh, a Yew Conservation Hedge Project is in place to plant around 2,200 yews, replacing the present hollies as a perimeter hedge. These plants have been collected from threatened wild populations and heritage trees.

> Scale of dragon, tooth of wolf,
> Witches' mummy, maw and gulf
> Of the ravined salt-sea shark,
> Root of hemlock digged i' th' dark,
> Liver of blaspheming Jew,
> Gall of goat and slips of yew
> Slivered in the moon's eclipse,
> Nose of Turk and Tartar's lips,
> Finger of birth-strangled babe
> Ditch-delivered by a drab,
> Make the gruel thick and slab.
> Add thereto a tiger's chaudron,
> For the ingredients of our cauldron.
>
> William Shakespeare, *Macbeth*, Act IV, Scene I

The History of the Yew

A yew tree stands for many centuries but it is very difficult to estimate the age of a particular specimen accurately. Suckering and intertwining are common, and these render the usual technique of ring counting very inaccurate. As a result, figures of 3,000 years are probably an overestimate, and a truer figure might be 1,000–2,000. However, a classic specimen has stood for many centuries in the village of Fortingall, Glen Lyon, Perthshire. Local folklore had it that it was an ancient preaching site (which is probably true) and that Pontius Pilate had been suckled beneath it when his father served as a Roman legionary in Scotland (which is probably false). It was visited by the eminent German botanist Alexander von Humboldt (1769–1859) and later by the toxicologist Robert Christison (1797–1882). The latter pronounced its age to be approximately 3,000 years. It stands to this day, although it was badly damaged when a fire was lit in its hollow trunk to celebrate Beltane on 1 May 1825.

Taxus baccata is thought to be a species indigenous to Europe and is widely distributed throughout the continent.

It grows well in northern temperate zones. The Celtic people are thought to have brought the tree to the south and west of Great Britain from Spain, where it is abundant. Julius Caesar records that the Druids preached the doctrine of the immortality of the soul, and that the yew was their sacred tree as well as a symbol of immortality. The Druid priest, as chief medicine man of the Celtic tribe, is said to have sat under the sacred tree and dispensed wisdom and justice. As a result, yews were often planted on sites regarded as holy by the Druids, a custom that was later adopted by Christians, who often took over sacred sites that pre-dated Christianity. Consequently, the yew is now frequently found in churchyards, usually on the south or south-west side of the church. As the tree was considered sacred, and invested with special powers, yew was also a favoured wood with which to make magic wands.

The Fortingall Yew, Glen Lyon, Perthshire, believed to be one of the oldest living things in Europe. Cuttings from the tree were recently planted at RBGE as part of the Yew Conservation Hedge Project.

Early Christians commonly appropriated local customs and folklore into their own traditions and liturgy. As the cypress tree had become the symbol of immortality in southern Europe, so did the yew in the north, with the green boughs of the yew representing renewal and eternal youth. During Holy Week, the week before Easter, if palm leaves were unavailable, yew twigs were worn in the caps of worshippers. The yew also gained a place in funeral solemnities. The bodies of the dead were often rubbed with an infusion of yew leaves, thought to be in an attempt both to preserve them and to guarantee their immortality.

In the Middle Ages, the yew was often associated with virginity and linked to the Virgin Mary. The tree is prone to develop fibrous, hair-like growths under the bark and on its roots, which were said to be symbolic of the Virgin Mary's hair. In many churches named after Saint Mary the Virgin, an honoured place was reserved for yew trees. At one time they were only clipped on 8 September, the feast of the Nativity of the Blessed Virgin Mary.

With all such powerful associations – death, life, immortality and the Blessed Virgin – it is not surprising that the local peasantry and farmers came to tolerate the yew, although they were fully aware of its toxic properties. They preferred the trees to be planted in the churchyard out of the reach of their cattle and horses. The planting of yew trees often predated the churches they now stand beside, and when the churches came to be built they were placed to the north or the north-east side of the tree. Robert Turner in his *Botanologia*, published in 1664, describes the yew as 'hot and dry' and claims that it 'will attract poysonous vapours and imbibe them'.[1] He thought that it was at the south

The title page of Robert Turner's 1664 *Botanologia* in which he repeated Dioscorides' statement that lying under the branches of a yew tree could cause death.

Taxine A

$$C_{35}H_{47}NO_{10}$$

and west sides of the church that gases ('will o' the wisps') were released from the putrefaction of decaying corpses. We now know that these gases are hydrogen sulphide, sulphur dioxide and methane. He believed that the gases would gather under the

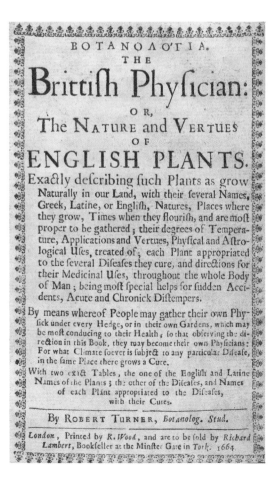

BOTANOΛOΓIA.
THE
Brittish Physician:
OR,
The NATURE and VERTUES
OF
ENGLISH PLANTS.

Exactly describing such Plants as grow Naturally in our Land, with their several Names, Greek, Latine, or English, Natures, Places where they grow, Times when they flourish, and are most proper to be gathered; their degrees of Temperature, Applications and Vertues, Physical and Astrological Uses, treated of; each Plant appropriated to the several Diseases they cure, and directions for their Medicinal Uses, throughout the whole Body of Man; being most special helps for sudden Accidents, Acute and Chronick Distempers.

By means whereof People may gather their own Physick under every Hedge, or in their own Gardens, which may be most conducing to their Health; so that observing the direction in this Book, they may become their own Physicians: For what Climate soever is subject to any particular Disease, in the same Place there grows a Cure.

With two exact Tables, the one of the English and Latine Names of the Plants; the other of the Diseases, and Names of each Plant appropriated to the Diseases, with their Cures.

By ROBERT TURNER, Botanolog. Stud.

London, Printed by R. Wood, and are to be sold by Richard Lambert, Bookseller at the Minster Gate in York. 1664.

Mary Evans Picture Library

English bowmen in the period of Edward IV's reign. Their bows were usually made of yew and, unbent, were taller than the height of a man.

branches of the yew before they were imbibed by the tree and that this concentration of poison could be deadly. Turner quoted the Greek physicians Dioscorides (c. AD 40–90) and Galen (c. AD 129–200), who had stated that lying under the branches of the yew could cause death. There were contrasting views. The botanist John Gerard (1545–1612), in his *Herball* of 1579, rashly denied all such claims stating that he had eaten his fill of the berries and slept under the branches, not once but often, and had not come to any harm.

The Yew and the Bow

Yew was the wood of choice for making the longbow. It is not known with any certainty which part of the yew tree the wood was cut from; some claim that the bows were made from the branches, others that the wood of the trunk was used. The best yew bows were derived not from trees grown in Britain but from those imported from Spain and Italy along with wine shipments. The export of yew

from Britain was forbidden by statute, a royal edict to maintain the inward supply in a time of great demand for bows. The oldest surviving yew longbow was found in 1990 at Rotten Bottom in Dumfries and Galloway. Radiocarbon dating suggests that it is around 6,000 years old and it is now on display in the National Museum of Scotland in Edinburgh. Even older is the yew spear tip found in 1911 in Clacton-on-Sea in Essex. The oldest surviving wooden artifact ever found in Britain, it is thought to date from Lower Palaeolithic times. The generic name for the yew, *Taxus,* is from the Latin word for the yew tree, perhaps derived from the Greek word *taxon*, meaning bow.

Toxicology of the Yew

All parts of the yew except the aril are poisonous. The basic poisonous alkaloids are called taxines, which are toxic to the heart and the walls of the stomach and gut. Drying does not destroy the toxicity of the leaves. The basic poison of the yew is called taxine A. Taxine B is chemically similar but exists in lower concentrations. There is no known antidote to either of these poisons, and so as a result the ingestion of around 50–100 g of leaf, and a smaller quantity of the seeds, is usually fatal.

This toxicity has been known since ancient times, when Scythian warriors used yew juice for the tips of their poison arrows. Julius Caesar also recorded what is perhaps the first historical case of poisoning by yew when Catibulus, king of the Eburones, a Germanic tribe in what is now part of Belgium, committed suicide by drinking its juice.

Farmers too have been aware for many centuries of the toxic effect of yew on their livestock and often destroy any trees found in the vicinity. In the 19th century the tree reappeared in large gardens and was valued for its evergreen leaves, attractive red 'berries' and the fact that they are one of the few conifers that can be cut down and will resprout. The seeds and leaves are the most dangerous part of the plant due to their content of the taxines, although the seeds are bitter and so are usually spat out when eaten by mistake. It is thought that taxines A and B can inhibit calcium and sodium transport in the muscular cells of the heart, producing fatal abnormalities in heart rhythm. It is worth noting that the taxels, the therapeutic compounds derived from the yew, can also on occasion cause cardiac toxicity.

The first description of yew poisoning in British medical literature appears to be in an 1836 edition of the *Lancet*. A child of three ingested yew berries, vomited some of them, then convulsed and died. The post mortem revealed that there were pathological changes in the stomach and gut. Four other children had also swallowed berries, but recovered after being given a strong emetic to cause them to vomit. There had also been three fatal cases in Manchester where yew leaves had been used therapeutically in order to eradicate intestinal worms.

The bright berries of *Taxus baccata* often attract children to eat them. The coloured aril is not poisonous but the seed inside is exremely toxic.

Since its original description, sporadic cases of poisoning have been reported. The symptoms of poisoning are nausea, vomiting and severe abdominal pain followed soon after by low blood pressure and fatal heart rhythms. A young woman of 16 who had been confined to a secure residential institution after several suicide attempts ate a handful of yew leaves from a tree in the grounds. A few hours later she developed various cardiac abnormalities but made a full recovery after treatment. A yew in the hospital grounds had been felled and was awaiting removal. Four other patients ate leaves from the felled tree but all recovered after immediate hospital treatment. This serves to emphasise that all yew leaves should be burned, even after the tree has been felled, if there is any risk to humans or animals.

Another example of yew being used as a means of suicide was reported in Ireland in 2006 in the *Irish Independent*. A young woman was found dead in her home after drinking a tea she had made. At first a post mortem could not find any reason for her death. No alcohol or drugs were discovered in her system. However, containers of seeds and the tea-like drink were found in her apartment. On examination by a taxonomist at the National Botanic Gardens at Glasnevin, Dublin, both were found to have derived from the yew. It appears that awareness of the yew's toxicity is increasing and that information is becoming more widespread on suicide-related websites.

The three witches from Shakespeare's *Macbeth*, who included 'slips of yew', amongst other poisonous and bizarre ingredients, in their brew.

The taxels

The yew is a veritable mixture of compounds, many of which have been identified, including taxines, taxols, taxusines, taxagifin and baccatins I, II and III. Until 1971 the toxic effects of the various members of the yew family were medical curiosities seen occasionally in accident and emergency departments. The situation changed dramatically in 1971 when an anti-cancer compound was isolated from the bark of the western or Pacific yew (*Taxus brevifolia* Nutt.). The structure of the compound was subsequently elucidated and it was named paclitaxel. A structurally close compound with similar anti-cancer activity has also been synthesised and named docetaxel. Paclitaxel demonstrated unique anti-cancer activity in disturbing microtubule formation and thereby inhibiting cell division.

The main problem faced by investigators of these compounds in the initial period of research was the low concentration of taxel in the yew (0.01% w/w). To obtain 1 kg of taxel would have required approximately 30,000 kg of bark and, as a consequence, *T. brevifolia* would have been extinct in the Pacific Northwest within a decade. However, a solution was within reach. At first the taxels were synthesised by a semi-synthetic route from 10-desacetylbaccatin. This is a renewable resource found in *T. baccata* and in *T. wallichiana* Zucc. (the Himalayan yew).

Taxol

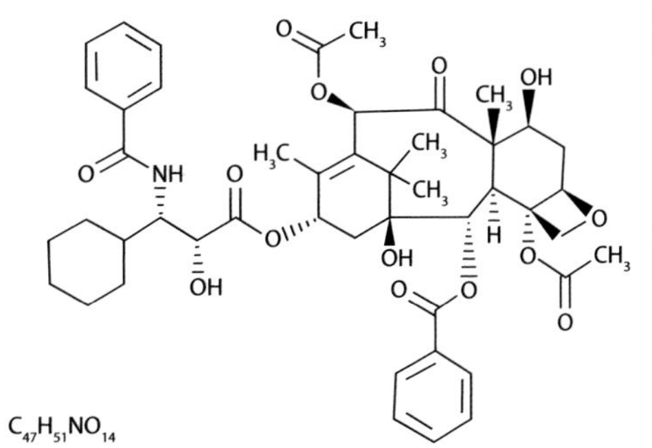

$C_{47}H_{51}NO_{14}$

Docetaxel

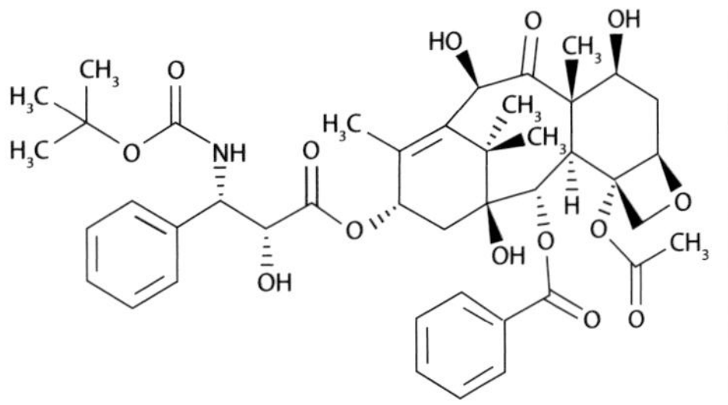

$C_{43}H_{53}NO_{14}$

A total synthesis from simple, readily available, organic compounds has now been achieved, reducing the environmental threat of extinction of important species of the tree.

The taxels have a broad spectrum of anti-cancer activity and have proven effective in treating a variety of cancers, including those that have acquired resistance to other anti-cancer chemicals.

Taxels from the yew have proved the most promising anti-cancer agents to emerge in the last several decades and are now a mainstay of anti-cancer treatment. People were rightly frightened of the yew in ancient and medieval times, with its powerful associations with death. Now, with the application of chemical science and the advent of these new powerful remedies for cancer, we can look at this ancient tree with new respect. The tree of death has indeed become a tree for life.

Colchicaceae.

Colchicum autumnale L.

WM. n. d. Nat.

25.

15 – The Autumn Crocus (*Colchicum autumnale*): An Islamic Medicine for Gout

Colchicum autumnale must rank as one of the first plants in Europe recognised to have a specific effect on a defined disease rather than on symptoms of a disease. That disease is gout, which has affected the great and the good over many centuries, including, for example, Hippocrates, Alexander the Great, Benjamin Franklin and King George IV. Indeed, in the 17th and 18th centuries one was not regarded as a man until one had experienced one's first attack of gout. Until *Colchicum* began to be used at the end of the 18th century there were no specific cures and the unfortunate victims were often drugged with laudanum (an opium solution) sweetened with port or sherry, which, if anything, only tended to make the condition worse.

The autumn crocus plant is in the recently established family Colchicaceae, but was formerly a member of the lily family (Lililaceae). Its taxonomic name is *Colchicum autumnale*, but it goes by more colourful common names including meadow saffron, naked ladies and naked boys. The species is a herbaceous perennial of the meadows of Europe and is thought to have originated in Colchis, a region of Georgia and northern Turkey on the eastern shore of the Black Sea. The plant has an unusual vegetative cycle. The flowers appear from the corm in September and October without leaves (hence the names naked ladies and naked boys). Following a winter resting period, the leaves appear together with the fertilised ovum, which resembles a nut. Each year a replacement corm develops at the expense of the parent plant.

Colchicum looks superficially like a true crocus; indeed, the autumn crocus is sometimes confused with the saffron crocus (*Crocus sativus*) and the wild crocus (*Crocus cartwrightianus*), but these are members of Iridaceae, the iris family. Other important members of the genus *Colchicum* include *C. cilicium*, *C. luteum* and *C. variegatum*, which do contain the active alkaloid colchicine but not in sufficient concentration to make extraction of the alkaloid commercially viable.

History of the Autumn Crocus

The autumn crocus plant has been known since ancient times. The Greeks were aware that it was a powerful poison. The Greek physician Dioscorides (c. AD 40–90) described it as a deadly toxin used by slaves to end their unhappy lives. The first definite description of the autumn crocus was given by the distinguished Byzantine physician Alexander of Tralles (c. 525–605). He recognised the action of *Colchicum* (or hermodactyl, as it was also known) on gout but suggested that it might not be effective for treating other forms of arthritis. Another 6th-century Byzantine physician, Aëtius of Amida, confirmed that with the correct dosage, arthritic pain could disappear within two days, and so some physicians began to call the plant *anima articulorum* ('soul of the joints').

Later, when the Muslims invaded and annexed Constantinople, their physicians continued to investigate *Colchicum*, both for its effect on gout and to confirm that it possessed aphrodisiac properties. The Muslim Empire then expanded into Spain and Italy, taking this knowledge of the plant with it. The pharmacopoeia from the Salerno school of medicine, produced in 12th-century Italy,

An engraving depicting the German Abbess and physician Hildegard of Bingen. A fascinating character, she condemned the use of *Colchicum* due to its association with Muslim physicians.

HILDEGARDIS a Virgin *Propheteſs*, Abbeſs of Sᵗ Rvperts Nunnerye. She died at Bingen Aᵒ Do: 1180 Aged 82 yeares.
W. Marſhall ſculpſit.

contained a description of the *Bulbus rusticus* (then the Latin name for *Colchicum*), its authors claiming that it was a successful remedy for arthritic gout.

In Europe, *Colchicum* then passed into its own Dark Age. There were a number of problems: obtaining the correct corms, drying and preparing them in an appropriate way and avoiding giving the patient an overdose. In addition, the work of the Muslim physicians was decried as heretical in a time of vicious religious warfare. Saint Hildegard of Bingen (1098–1179), the German nun and polymath who had a great interest in plants, condemned *Colchicum* in her pharmacopoeia, calling it a deadly heretical poison and not a health-giving drug. As she was a noted authority on medicines, her views carried a great deal of weight and the plant began to be mistrusted.

In Great Britain hermodactyl appears in the first edition of the *Pharmacopoeia Londinensis* in 1618 but was then omitted in later editions until it reappeared in that of 1788. A major influence here was the physician Thomas Sydenham (1624–1689) who, himself a sufferer of gout, declared that all purging treatments generally had the effect of 'bring[ing] on what they were meant to keep off'.[1] Purgatives were thus abandoned and *Colchicum* was once again condemned to oblivion for more than a century. The situation changed radically in 1780 when Nicolas Husson, an officer in the French army, marketed a patent medicine which came to be known as *l'eau médicinale d'Husson* (Husson's medicinal water). Although he would not disclose its active constituents, he claimed that his medicine had specific effects on gout and many other diseases and disorders. The medical profession opposed its use and its sale was banned for a time. However, it soon

THOMAS   SYDENHAM
Maria Beale pinxit.   A. Blooteling Sculp.

A portrait of Thomas Sydenham, the physician and gout sufferer who initially spoke against the use of *Colchicum* for gout but eventually found it effective in his own case.

became very clear that it was indeed extremely active in the treatment of gout and the ban was later lifted. Edwin Godden Jones, a doctor from Hampshire, brought the remedy to England in 1808 and in 1810 produced a short treatise on its use entitled *An Account of the Remarkable Effects of the Eau Médicinale d'Husson in the Gout*. In 1814, a Dr James Watt discovered that the active principle in the water was colchicine and Husson's secret was at last revealed.

Scientific advance assumed a more rapid pace as the age of modern chemistry dawned. Carl-Wilhelm Scheele (1742–1786), an eminent German-Swedish chemist, said that colchicine increased the excretion of lithic (uric) acid, and in 1820 the French chemists Pierre-Joseph Pelletier (1788–1842) and Joseph-Bienaimé Caventou (1795–1877) succeeded in isolating colchicine from *Colchicum*. Subsequently, in 1844, the French chemist Alfred Houdé (1854–1919) crystallised the alkaloid from extracts and tinctures of the corm. The specific effect of colchicine on gout could then be established and, as Alexander of Tralles had forecast over 1,000 years earlier, it was revealed that some types of arthritis responded to colchicine and some, like rheumatoid arthritis and osteoarthritis, did not. With further advances in science the tinctures and galenical (herb-based) preparations used were soon replaced by stable and reliable materials and accurate dosages established. Although the therapeutic index (the margin between the therapeutic dose and the toxic dose) for this drug was found by many physicians to be small, colchicine nonetheless dominated the therapeutic scene for gout until the 1960s. It was not until then that allopurinol, a good preventative treatment, was developed, followed in the 1970s by the first effective anti-inflammatory drug, ibuprofen. Colchicine

may now be a second-line drug, but it has made a long and honourable contribution to the study of gout and the history of medicine.

How Colchicine Works

In the latter years of the 19th century, Biaggio Pernice (1854–1906), a Sicilian pathologist, conducted experiments involving poisoning dogs with colchicine. When he looked at post-mortem specimens under a microscope he found signs of increased cell division. He also saw that one phase of the cell division cycle was missing and suggested that colchicine was what is now known as a mitotic spindle poison (one that interrupts cell division). These prescient observations remained in limbo for the next 50 years until further research work was carried out on the effects of colchicine on cell division. This stimulated work on abnormal cell division in cancer and the use of colchicine derivations to treat leukaemia, which in turn led to the discovery of the vinca alkaloids in the periwinkle (*Vinca major* and *Vinca minor*) and the taxol alkaloids in the yew (see Chapter 14), which are now widely used in cancer treatment.

Pierre-Joseph Pelletier, one of the French chemists who isolated colchicine from *Colchicum*, part of the advance which saw colchicine dominate the therapeutic scene for gout until the 1960s.

Colchicine

Colchicine is an alkaloid which binds to chromosomes and damages them. This action inhibits cell division and also interferes with cellular migration. It would appear that a higher concentration of colchicine is needed to stop cell division than is required to inhibit cellular migration. In patients with gout, colchicine does not affect either the production of uric acid in the liver or the deposition of the acid in the joints. The specific effect appears to be preventing the white cells from dividing and migrating, and thus initiating the reactions which mediate the inflammatory reaction in the joint. The white blood cells continue to ingest the crystals of uric acid, but they no longer lead to acute inflammation. Colchicine is rapidly but poorly absorbed from the gastrointestinal tract. The drug and its metabolites undergo extensive change both in the gut and in the

Colchicine

Colchicine methyl ether

$C_{22}H_{25}NO_6$

liver. It is thought that this cycling of the alkaloid through the liver into the bile can contribute materially to prolonged damage to the gut that occurs after an overdose.

Therapeutic and Other Uses of Colchicine

More than two centuries after Husson patented his medicinal water, what is the place of colchicine in modern medicine and science? First, the treatment of gout today depends largely on the use of anti-inflammatory drugs for the acute attack and allopurinol for the prevention of further attacks. In patients who are intolerant of these drugs, however, colchicine still has a limited but definite place. Perhaps the most fascinating use of colchicine today is to treat the condition of Familial Mediterranean Fever (FMF). FMF is an inherited condition prevalent among people originating from the Mediterranean region, especially those of Armenian, Arab, Turkish and Jewish ancestry, and is characterised by recurrent attacks of inflammation in the chest and abdomen. This

inflammation is sometimes accompanied by arthritis and a skin rash. In around 20 per cent of cases, kidney failure occurs over a period of a few years. The only effective treatment for this rare and unusual disorder is colchicine. It substantially reduces the number of attacks of fever and helps to prevent kidney failure.

In horticulture, colchicine acts on the cells of plants to inhibit the separation of daughter chromosomes at cell division. Plant cells tolerate higher concentrations of colchicine than can be used in humans. This is extremely useful in horticulture, where it is used for its ability to inhibit separation of chromosomes when ovules are formed. This results in plants with three (triploid), four (tetraploid) or more sets of chromosomes instead of the normal two (diploid). These 'polyploid' plants often have advantages over the parent plant in terms of hardiness, pest resistance and yield.

Gout

Gout was recognised by Hippocrates (460–370 BC), who regarded the disorder as an excessive accumulation of phlegm, one of the four basic bodily substances known as humours. Phlegm was thought to flow into the affected joints, producing painful inflammation as a result of sexual excess or too rich a diet combined with a sedentary life. The name gout was derived from the Latin *gutta*, meaning a drop, symbolising the flow of drops of phlegm into the joint or skin. According to one of one of Hippocrates' aphorisms, 'a young man does not take the gout until he indulges in coitus'.[2] As a result, until as late as the 18th century, castration was considered a suitable treatment for chronic sufferers of gout.

Initially, treatment was directed towards removing the evil humours from the body by various means which included bleeding, vomiting, increasing urine flow and, in particular, purging. Two of the common purgatives employed in ancient times were scammony (*Convolvulus scammonia*) and white hellebore (*Veratrum album*). It is likely that *Colchicum* was used first as yet another purgative but then proved to have a more specific and salutary effect. Several distinguished individuals attested to its efficacy, including Sir Joseph Banks

An 1824 William Heath cartoon depicting the gouty George IV sitting in front of portraits of himself that hint at his past extravagance. The King's decision to take *Colchicum* for his gout partly led to its acceptance in English society.

Gout

(1743–1820), then President of the Royal Society of London, and the Prince Regent, later King George IV. The latter had been reliant on the opium poppy, and his decision to take *Colchicum*, initially against the wishes of his physicians, helped to make Husson's water respectable in the upper strata of society. Indeed, the King is said to have recommended *Colchicum* to the Bourbon Prince Louis with such good effect that in 1816 Louis was able to leave Richmond in Surrey to assume the throne of France, as Louis XVIII, following the defeat of Napoleon at Waterloo.

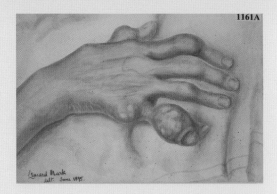

A watercolour of the right hand of a woman suffering from chronic gout. The hand has become disfigured by a tophus and the skin over the tophus has ulcerated.

A 1799 coloured etching by James Gillray simply entitled *The Gout*. The devil biting and clawing at the inflamed toe goes some way to depicting the agony experienced by sufferers of the disease.

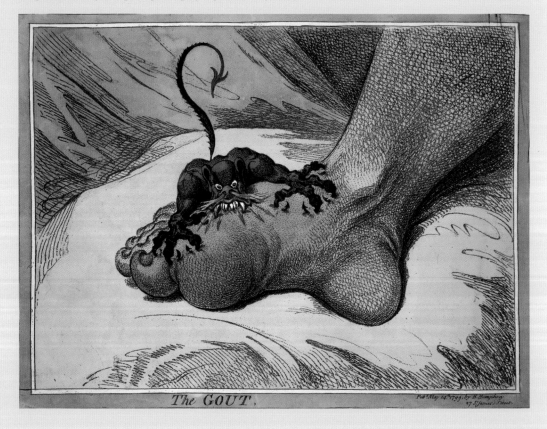

The GOUT.

Toxicology of the Autumn Crocus

The toxic dose of colchicine in human beings is about 10 mg and ingesting 40 mg of the pure alkaloid is nearly always fatal within a matter of days. The plant or its parts are sometimes ingested accidentally, for example when its leaves are mistaken for wild garlic (*Allium ursinum*), or the corm is confused with a walnut. In 2001 a case was reported of a woman admitted to hospital suffering from severe digestive disorders having used what she thought was wild garlic to bake a pie she had seen on a television cookery programme. The medical staff were able to ascertain that she had confused the ingredient with the autumn crocus and treated her accordingly with activated charcoal. Cases of colchicine poisoning have also been reported after people have eaten the tiger lily (*Gloriosa superba*), another member of the lily family, which also contains the alkaloid.

A historic case of intentional poisoning using *Colchicum* came to light in London in 1862 when Catherine Wilson was hanged for murder by poisoning. Wilson worked as a housekeeper to a Captain Mawer, a man who became reliant on her care as he suffered from gout. He promised his faithful servant that she would be recognised in his will and shortly afterwards was found dead, having seemingly taken an overdose of the colchicine he had used to ease his condition. It was not until nine years later, and following the deaths of four more of Wilson's friends and employers, that the serial poisoner was brought to justice. She was hanged at Newgate Prison in front of an enormous crowd, taking her place in the history

An inner court of Newgate Prison, London. Catherine Wilson was hanged there in 1862 for multiple murders, one of which she carried out using *Colchicum* to poison her victim.

books as the last woman to be publicly executed in London.

Acute overdose of the alkaloid first produces nausea, vomiting and diarrhoea; liver and kidney failure may follow. All the blood-forming elements of the bone marrow may be depressed, including the white cells, which often results in septicaemia. Muscular weakness and ascending paralysis of the nervous system can occur, and death usually results from a combination of respiratory and cardiac failure. In view of the effects of colchicine on cell division, it is interesting to note that there have been cases of delayed alopecia (loss of hair on the scalp and body) and a low or absent sperm count. These affected tissues both have a rapid rate of cell division. When Catherine Wilson was committing her murders in the 1860s there were no specific tests to either detect or measure the level of colchicine in a body during the post mortem.

The German physician Richard Ehrlich (1854–1915) devoted his research towards finding what later became known as magic bullets – chemical substances which would target and kill only the organism intended. Colchicine, a pivotal compound of pharmacology, is one of these magic bullets, having a unique action to relieve a specific disease, in this case gout. Its discovery would influence later work on penicillin, as scientists reasoned that if colchicine could get to the heart of the matter then why shouldn't other substances be able to do the same for other important diseases? For this alone, *Colchicum* and colchicine deserve an honourable mention in this book.

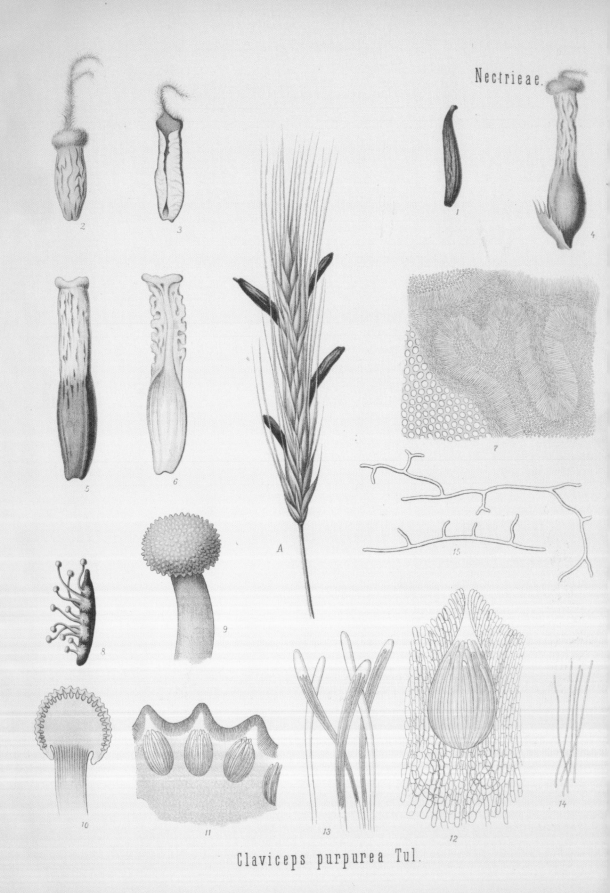

Nectrieae.

Claviceps purpurea Tul.

155

16 – The Ergot Fungus (*Claviceps purpurea*): Unlocking a Treasure Chest

The ergot fungus has a long and complex history. Ergot has been variously referred to by pharmacologists as a gold mine and a treasure chest. These descriptions have been attached to the fungus for two main reasons: first, because of the large number of active compounds that it contains and second, because of the catalytic effect that the discovery of these substances would have on the development of the medical sciences in general and pharmacology in particular.

*C*laviceps purpurea is an interesting fungus, a member of the family Ascomycetes that is composed of fungi that produce sexual spores in flask-shaped chambers. The word 'ergot' probably derives from the Latin word *articulum* (articulation or joint) via the Old French *argot* (cockspur, suggesting the shape of the sclerotium of the fungus). A number of grasses are subject to attack by this fungus; rye (*Secale cereale*) is particularly susceptible, but others, such as wheat, barley and oats, are much more resistant. As a result, the history of ergot and ergotism (poisoning caused by the ergot fungus) is inextricably linked to the history and distribution of rye.

The History of the Fungus

Ergot was known to the ancients in Mesopotamia, where it infected grasses grown in early farming settlements. It resurfaced in medieval Europe during the many famines when peasants were forced to eat grain infested with black cockspurs. The first unequivocal description of the fungus and its action was that by German botanist Adam Lonitzer (1528–1586) in his *Kräuterbuch* (book of herbs) of 1582 in which, in an appendix on rye, he states, 'There are long, black, hard, arrow pegs on the ears, internally white, often protruding like long nails from between the grains in

the ear.'[1] Lonitzer also mentioned that these hard pegs were foul-smelling and that they had been used to cause contractions in the womb and hence to induce or accelerate labour.

The first illustration of the sclerotium of the fungus appears to be that of the Swiss botanist Gaspard Bauhin (1560–1624) in his *Theatrum Botanicum* of 1658. The word 'ergot' was used for the first time in a 1683 publication entitled *The Weekly Memorials for the Ingenious*, where it is described as 'that malignity breeding in the ears of corn [sic] which contains certain black grains called, in Sologne, Ergots'.[2] Sologne is a region of north-central France where the cultivation of rye grass was widespread. In 1791, the physician and poet Erasmus Darwin (1731–1802), father of Charles, referred to ergot in his long poem *The Botanic Garden*, mentioning 'deep-rooted mould and ergot's horn uncouth'. Darwin still found it necessary to explain ergot to his readers in a footnote, saying that it was a disease 'affecting rye in France (commonly) and in England (occasionally)'.[3]

Rye was originally the bread grain of the Teutonic nations, while in Britain it was somewhat despised and regarded as a food fit only for the poor. The chief rye-growing area of Europe, where millions of acres were under cultivation, was a long belt extending from Holland and the Low Countries through Germany to Austria and what was then

Czechoslovakia. The cultivation of rye then moved into Poland and Russia, spreading as far east as the Ural Mountains. By contrast, between the two World Wars only 50,000 acres of rye grass were cultivated in England, chiefly in Lancashire, Yorkshire and the Cheshire Plain. This resulted in ergotism being a common disease in Germany and Russia, but relatively rare in Britain.

For a considerable period no one could explain what caused the formation of the black cockspurs on rye. In the early 18th century it was suggested that it was a parasitic infection, but what the parasite was remained a mystery. Eventually, in 1711, the French chemist Claude Joseph Geoffroy (1685–1752), and in 1764 the German botanist Otto von Münchhausen (1716–1774) suggested that the parasitic infection was in fact a fungus. The invention of the compound microscope and the development of germination techniques at the beginning of the 19th century enabled the nature and behaviour of this fungus to be established. First, sclerotia were allowed to germinate, producing what were clearly fructifications (spore-bearing parts). In 1853, Louis René Tulasne (1815–1885), a French botanist,

described the full life cycle of ergot in an article entitled *Mémoire sur l'ergot des glumacées.*

The first obvious effect of the parasite attacking the grass is the so-called 'honeydew', a sticky yellow solution which, when secreted by the infected plant ovary, exudes as drops between the affected glumes (the outer sterile husks) of the rye. The next stage in the cycle is the development of the black sclerotium, the cockspur. Under normal conditions, the sclerotia fall to the ground at the time of harvesting the grain, lying dormant until the following spring when they are activated by warmer temperatures. They can then undergo either sexual or asexual processes of reproductive propagation. Eventually, structures called asci are formed, releasing ascospores (spores contained within the asci) into the air. Clouds of these spores are forcibly shot away from the fungus body to a height of 7–15 cm and distributed randomly by the wind or by insects. In 1856, a French botanist called Michel-Charles Durieu de Maisonneuve (1796–1878) was able to infect rye flowers with *Claviceps* ascospores in the laboratory for the first time. This was the final key to unlocking the mystery that had baffled botanists for a century.

The Growth of Ergot

A serious infestation with *Claviceps*, such as might cause an epidemic of clinical ergotism, is produced by an unusual conjunction of climatic circumstances. The two important factors are a wet season, which favours germination of the sclerotia, followed by a dry and windy spell, which favours the dissemination of the ascospores. Rye is more susceptible to *Claviceps* infestation than other cereals because it depends largely on cross-fertilisation for its propagation, much more so than other grasses. It therefore opens its glumes to accept airborne or insect-borne pollen and as a consequence is also open to the ascospores of ergot. The fungus causes considerable damage to rye grass. As much

An SEM of the fruiting bodies of the ergot fungus (*Claviceps purpurea*). Fruiting bodies are the sexual reproductive structure of fungi.

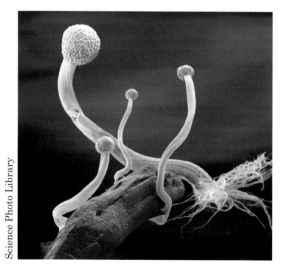

Science Photo Library

as 50 per cent of the grain may be lost and in areas such as Russia, where rye was a staple food, it could result in famine. The elimination of ergot from parasitised rye can be achieved only with considerable difficulty and at great expense.

At the end of the 19th century, when ergot began to be used in medicine, it became necessary to facilitate its growth artificially. Two methods were adopted: first, shaking the stems of the rye and second, pulling the ears of the grass between the fingers. These manoeuvres proved to be extremely labour-intensive. An alternative procedure was to spray the flowers with a dilute solution of the fungal spores. Eventually, yields of ergot as high as 500 kg per hectare were obtained.

Ergotism

In the Middle Ages it was suggested that there were two forms of clinical ergotism brought on by the ingestion of infested plant material: the gangrenous and the convulsive. The gangrenous form tended to occur west of the Rhine, the convulsive to the east. At first it was thought that the two forms were caused by different chemical agents in different types of the fungus, but by the early 19th century, it was widely accepted that ergotised rye was responsible for all forms of ergotism. Attempts were made to separate the healthy from the mouldy grain, but this proved technically difficult; unscrupulous farmers and millers would often not take the necessary steps to exclude the mould, resulting in the sale of poisonous rye.

Gangrenous ergotism ran a definite course. Initially, the patient would complain of general lassitude accompanied by pain in one or more limbs. Over the next few weeks, the affected limb would become swollen and inflamed, later accompanied by violent burning pains. These pains were so common and specific in the Middle Ages that ergotism was given names such as Saint Anthony's fire. Educated Latin speakers knew it as *sacer ignis* (sacred fire).

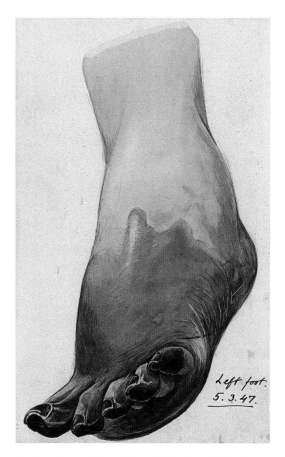

A watercolour of the swollen and discoloured foot of a patient suffering from gangrene. Gangrene is one of the symptoms of ergotism; the fungus irreversibly contracts the arterial blood supply, stopping oxygen from getting to the tissues.

Sensations of heat and cold would alternate in the limb, which would then become numb. The skin turned cold and livid, and red or purple blisters would appear. The diseased part of the limb became gangrenous and the sufferer would often lose fingers and toes.

The other type of ergotism, called convulsive ergotism, had as its initial symptoms a feeling of heaviness in the head and limbs accompanied by mild diarrhoea, followed by a numbness in the hands and feet and a tingling sensation or pins and needles in the limbs. At a later stage of the illness, patients complained of twitching in the muscles around the mouth and eye.

In mild cases of the disease symptoms abated at this stage, but in more severe cases the syndrome took a violent turn, with spasms similar to those suffered during an epileptic fit. In the severe form the patient did not sleep, developed multiple convulsions and eventually died. Some patients, however, managed to recover; the overall mortality in this form of ergotism ranged from 10 to 20 per cent, surprisingly low in an era when intensive care support and anti-convulsant drugs were not available. The mania and hallucinations which often accompanied the poisoning have been linked to events such as the Great Fear in France, an outbreak of mass hysteria following a peasant revolt at the beginning of the French Revolution, and even to the Salem witch trials, although such conclusions can only ever be speculative.

This bottle of ergot was produced in London and the instructions state that it is to be used only under medical supervision. While useful in inducing contractions in pregnant women, ergot could also precipitate miscarriage.

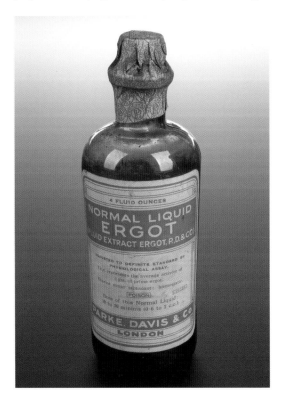

Ergot and Pregnancy

When ergotism affected women who were breastfeeding, the flow of milk often stopped completely and did not return. The ergot alkaloids can prevent the production of prolactin, the hormone that stimulates milk production. Ergot also seemed to have effects on pregnancy. Midwives had used powdered ergot for many years during the 17th and 18th centuries to accelerate labour and prevent uterine haemorrhage, but the evidence that it worked was largely anecdotal. In the 18th century this powdered preparation of ergot was called *pulvis ad partum* (literally 'powder of birth'). It had a powerful effect on the uterus, causing it to contract. If too large a dose was given, however, obstructed labour and signs of ergotism could occur. Several major advances in this field took place in the United States during the 19th century. In 1808, John Stearns (1770–1847), an American physician, published an article in which he claimed that his ergot preparation 'expedited lingering parturition [birth] and saved the accoucheur [the obstetrician] a considerable amount of time', without causing any bad effects on either the mother or the infant.[4] A further stimulus to the development of ergot was given by another American physician, Oliver Prescott (1762–1827), in 1813, when he published a pamphlet entitled *On the natural history and medicinal effects of the Secale cornutum or ergot*. This essay was so well received that it was translated into several European languages and as a result, the use of powder of ergot spread rapidly throughout France and later Germany. The United States pharmacopoeia of 1820 was the first to include ergot, followed by those of Italy, Greece, Great Britain and France. Many of these preparations were not standardised, and only that of the United States had its total alkaloid content measured. As a result the effects of the American ergot were reasonably reproducible, in contrast to those used in other countries.

A Chemical Factory

Ergot is a chemical factory containing everything from the simplest of compounds, such as amines and amino acids, to the most complex polycyclic alkaloids. At the last count, there were more than 200 clearly identified chemical compounds in a single extract of the fungus. Although it is widely recognised that the pharmacological activity largely resides in the alkaloid fraction of ergot, it was not fully appreciated that water (or saline) extracts could also contain powerful vasodilators, for example acetylcholine (a cholinergic) and histamine, and powerful vasoconstrictors such as tyramine (an adrenergic).

The chemical techniques of the 19th century were simply not advanced enough to isolate the active substances reproducibly. Moreover, when the 'substance' was obtained and crystallised, the analytical techniques were not specific enough to determine the side chain substituents of the closely related polycyclic compounds, such as so-called 'ergotoxine' which was identified early in this process and proved to be a mixture of alkaloids and not a pure substance. This was a formidable impasse which would take another 40 years of sustained effort to overcome.

Ergot contains many alkaloids and only one of them, ergometrine, has a pronounced effect on the uterus. It is no surprise, therefore, that some preparations of ergot were all but useless. There was controversy surrounding the efficacy of ergot throughout the whole of the 19th century, which would only be settled by the English pharmacologist Henry Hallett Dale (1875–1968) and colleagues, who, working alongside a team of Swiss scientists in the early years of the 20th century, proceeded to describe ergotamine and ergometrine.

Ergotamine

It took some time for ergotamine to be successfully isolated and fully characterised. Its complete structure was not established until 1961, although various scientists had been working on it for nearly 50 years. In spite of all this, in 1926 it was used for the first time to treat vascular headaches and proved highly successful. In 1938, the experimental use of ergotamine to treat migraine with aura was given a strong theoretical basis by the American physicians John R Graham (1909–1990) and Harold Wolff

(1898–1962), who demonstrated that its effect in reducing headache in migraine closely paralleled the fall in pulse amplitude in the extracranial arteries (those outside the skull). Initially ergotamine was found to be safe in younger patients but when its use was extended to older patients, dangerous side effects appeared.

A number of these older patient groups were shown to be particularly susceptible to the toxic effects of ergotamine, including those with high blood pressure, vascular disease, and liver and kidney damage. More recently, ergotamine and its derivatives have been found to produce fibrosis in the valves of the heart which may cause life-threatening heart failure. Prolonged and excessive constriction results in damage to the blood vessels. As a consequence, platelets adhere to the vessel wall, a clot is formed and thrombosis occurs. This sequence of events is reminiscent of the gangrenous ergotism caused by rye grass infected with *Claviceps purpurea*. Once started, the process of gangrenous ergotism is usually irreversible. For these reasons ergotamine is no longer the first-choice drug for migraine and has been replaced by the triptans, a class of drugs that constrict cranial blood vessels.

LSD

The German scientist Albert Hofmann who isolated the hallucinogenic drug LSD in 1943.

© STR/Keystone/Corbis

The story of lysergic acid diethylamide (LSD) began in 1938, when Swiss chemists Arthur Stoll (1887–1971) and Albert Hofmann (1906–2008), working at Sandoz Pharmaceuticals in Basel, Switzerland, succeeded in partially synthesising ergometrine. In the course of their research one of the compounds that emerged as a by-product was LSD. Five years later, when Hofmann was synthesising a new batch of LSD, he was overcome by a remarkable but not unpleasant state of intoxication: 'There surged upon me an uninterrupted stream of fantastic images of extraordinary plasticity and vividness, accompanied by an intense kaleidoscopic play of colours'.[5] This wore off gradually over the next few hours.

Hofmann immediately surmised that the LSD he had been working on could have been responsible for this curious hallucinatory attack. He also concluded that he must have been contaminated by a very small dose which he had accidentally either ingested or inhaled. Accordingly, he decided to embark upon a programme of experiments in which he took gradually increasing doses of LSD by mouth. The first dose he took seemed minute at the time, but in the light of many further observations it turned out to be a large overdose.

The effects of this first deliberate dose were indeed dramatic. Hofmann developed vertigo, visual hallucinations and motor agitation (fidgeting), followed by paralysis. Everything in the vicinity seemed to sway backwards and forwards or from side to side. A short time later, colours appeared to change very rapidly from one hue to another. Another effect was the phenomenon of synaesthesia, causing sounds, for example that of a passing car, to be transformed into optical hallucinations. Gradually, over a period of six to eight hours, the effects wore off and, following a good sleep, Hofmann's mental function returned to normal.

The publication of these results in 1947 caused something of a sensation. Academics working in the fields of psychiatry, psychology and neurobiology seized upon the compound and thousands of experiments were carried out on animals, healthy volunteers and psychotic patients.

Ergometrine

As mentioned above, ergot had been known for some time to be useful both during and after childbirth. From research in the United States in the early part of the 19th century it had been established that fresh powdered ergot produced a marked contraction of the uterus. But when the first substances were isolated from ergot their effects on uterine contraction were not pronounced. Something was missing. In the early 1930s, an obstetrician named John Chassar Moir (1900–1977) was convinced that a powerful uterine stimulant could be derived from ergot. He discussed this with pharmacologist Henry Hallett Dale (1875–1968), proposing an experiment using postpartum women as subjects. As a result of these experiments a pure crystalline substance, ergometrine, was isolated by research chemist Harold Dudley (1887–1935) in Dale's laboratory. Ergometrine proved to be highly effective in inducing labour and in preventing and controlling serious postpartum haemorrhage. Many lives were saved

After an initial wave of enthusiasm it was found that the drug appeared to make psychotic patients worse and in normal individuals could induce a damaging psychiatric state, particularly if taken repeatedly in large doses. This permanent psychotic reaction seemed to be associated with uncontrolled consumption of the drug in adolescents who had obtained the compound illicitly. Not only were there chronic psychiatric risks, but a number of individuals had serious acute reactions even after taking a single dose. A number of dangerous accidents were reported when people who had taken the drug thought they could fly. In their intoxicated state, they would leap from high places such as windows, balconies and roofs with the inevitable disastrous consequences.

Hofmann admitted later in his life that he had spent far too much of his time studying LSD. He was no doubt seduced by the idea that if he could produce a schizophrenia-like syndrome with LSD he could not be far from finding the cause of the psychosis and therefore perhaps a cure, although this did not transpire. He was one of the greatest analytic and synthetic chemists of the 20th century and his contribution will not be forgotten.

Ergometrine

$C_{19}H_{23}N_3O_2$

Ergotamine

$C_{33}H_{35}N_5O_5$

thanks to this discovery of the beneficial effect of ergometrine. It is still one of the mainstays of obstetric therapeutics and is widely used throughout the developed world.

Ergot has a long history that spans the period from ancient times in Mesopotamia to the present day. Initially it was known only as a poisonous fungus and had no therapeutic uses until the early 18th century, when it was discovered that in powdered form it could induce labour and stem postpartum haemorrhage. Knowledge of the chemistry of the powder lagged far behind the studies of its action in pregnant women. That knowledge would not advance at all until the 20th century, when groups in London and Basel began to isolate its pure alkaloids, including ergotamine and ergometrine. Only when the chemical cloud was gradually refined into its powerful therapeutic entities could the true value of this treasure chest be made known.

Afterword

In the American Pharmacopoeia of 1914, of the ten most widely used drugs only two were of plant origin, codeine and digoxin. It was widely predicted at that time that all plant drugs would become obsolete by 1960. This forecast has been shown to be completely wrong. As new synthetic compounds proved more difficult to make and develop so attention has become more concentrated once again on the bountiful treasures of the plant kingdom. Of one thing I am sure, there are still many useful undiscovered compounds out there, both in the plant kingdom and in the marine and invertebrate group. We must act now or many opportunities to discover them will be lost forever. This is a particular threat of the present rapid extinction process. Future generations must ensure that the plant and animal biospheres are preserved, not only for their intrinsic worth, but also to minimise the risk that compounds which may be valuable to mankind will be lost.

As explained in the introduction, this series of articles started by accident when I read about the potential use of paclitaxel in treating cancer. I realised I had stumbled on an area of scientific endeavour about which I knew very little. There was no particular pattern to the plants I chose to study, except perhaps their association on the one hand with therapeutics and toxicology, and on the other with mythology and history. I have learned much about all these areas and I hope that I have been able to convey in this volume some sense of the excitement generated by the hunt for, and the discovery of, these plants.

Botanical knowledge has illuminated the sciences of pharmacology, toxicology and therapeutics. In turn these sciences have identified plant sources of alkaloids which have led to searches for other plants (often unrelated taxonomically) which can be more easily available. Botany and medicine are inextricably interlinked as the history of the 16 plants and fungi here shows. So I wish to close by joining the old medical salutation *Floreat res medica* to a new one: *Floreat res botanica.*

Glossary of Chemical Compounds

Acetylcholine is one of the main transmitters of the brain. When an electrical signal reaches the end of a nerve fibre it triggers the release of acetylcholine which crosses the synaptic gap and locks onto specific receptors which are then activated to slow the heart or activate muscular contraction, for example. These receptors are called the cholinergic receptors.

Acid is a substance that turns blue litmus paper red. Acids combine with alkalis to form neutral salts. When dissolved in water they form hydrogen ions.

Adrenaline (known in the United States as **epinephrine**) is a catecholamine produced by the adrenal gland and certain parts of the brain in mammals. It is involved in the 'fight or flight' response. It acts on the adrenergic receptors and opposes the actions of acetylcholine on the body; for example, adrenaline dilates the pupil while acetylcholine constricts it.

Alkali is a substance that turns red litmus paper blue. Alkalis combine with acids to form neutral salts. They dissolve in water to form hydroxyl ions.

Alkaloids are alkaline bases found in many plants. They readily form salts with many acids, for example hyoscine with hydrochloric acid forms hyoscine hydrochloride and with bromic acid forms hyoscine bromide. They compose the majority of the plant poisons and include such classical poisons as atropine and physostigmine. Their names usually end in -ine and they interact with the cholinergic and adrenergic receptors.

Anticholinergic alkaloids block the effect of acetylocholine on their receptors. Important examples include atropine and hyoscine. Atropine is an alkaloid of the tropane family. It is obtained from *Atropa belladonna* (deadly nightshade) and classically dilates the pupil. It is also an antidote for poisoning with physostigmine, the active alkaloid from the Calabar bean, and vice versa.

Artemesinin This is a very effective anti-malarial compound found in the sweet wormwood (*Artemesia annua*). This plant was known to Chinese herbalists for many hundreds of years. They valued it for the treatment of the fever associated with the rainy season. It is now known that this is the peak period for the expansion of the population of the *Anopheles* mosquito, the vector for *Plasmodia* (the protozoan parasites that cause clinical malaria). The pure compound artemesinin was isolated in 1971 by Chinese scientists and initially they guarded this secret closely. It is now used worldwide in combination with other anti-malarial drugs, such as quinine.

Atropine is the active alkaloid obtained from *Atropa belladonna* (deadly nightshade). It is an anticholinergic drug and therefore causes the heart rate to accelerate, the mouth to dry and the pupils to dilate. It reverses the action of physostigmine (a cholinergic drug) and can be used as an antidote in nerve gas poisoning.

Chirality is a property of certain molecules where, despite the same number of atoms, when seen in three dimensions they are mirror images of each other. Such pairs of molecules can deviate polarised light either to the right (dextro, d or +) or to the left (laevo, l or -). Dextro and laevo are the Latin names for right and left respectively and are still in common use. These mirror-image molecules are very important in toxicology because, for example, l-hyoscine is poisonous whereas d-hyoscine is not   and one molecule may even oppose the action of its mirror image.

Cholinesterase is an enzyme or biological catalyst which normally destroys acetylcholine in the synaptic gap. If this enzyme is inhibited in the synaptic gap by an alkaloid such as physostigmine, then acetylcholine will accumulate and exert a greater effect on the receptor. Hence physostigmine is called a cholinergic drug.

Chromatography (literally colour writing) is a very commonly used method for separating molecules. Separation techniques include those on chemical columns; filter paper; glass plates (thin layer); and by gas. The gas chromatographic process can be linked to mass spectroscopy to identify the components after they have been separated. This technique was used in the poisoning case in Chapter 1 to identify minute amounts of l-hyoscine which were found in the poisoner's car.

Colchicine The alkaloid derived from the autumn crocus (*Colchicum autumnale*). It has a powerful inhibitory action on cell division, notably in the white blood cell, and has acted as a springboard for the development of anti-cancer agents in the treatment of leukaemia.

Compound In chemistry this denotes a combination of elements; for example, sodium chloride (common salt) is a compound of the metal sodium and the gas chlorine.

Congener (chemical) A chemical congener is a similar compound. For example, sodium hydroxide (caustic soda NaOH) is a congener of potassium hydroxide (caustic potash KOH).

Curare is an impure extract of the South American liana (climbing vine) *Chondrodendron tomentosum*. It is the source of the alkaloid d-tubocurarine which is a paralytic poison. A famous arrow poison, it was used to kill small mammals and birds for the pot. It is also an antidote to strychnine and has been used in the treatment of tetanus.

Digitalis, Digoxin and Digitoxin Digitalis leaf is the powdered extract of the leaves of either of two foxgloves: *Digitalis purpurea* or *Digitalis lanata* (purple and broad-leaved respectively). From these two plants are obtained two medicinal compounds, digoxin and digitoxin, known as cardiac glycosides. These compounds act upon the heart to increase its muscular contraction and hence they are both widely used in the treatment of cardiac failure with its associated oedema (fluid retention).

Docetaxel and Paclitaxel These compounds are obtained from the yews. The main sources are *Taxus baccata* (the European yew), *Taxus brevifolia* (the Pacific yew) and *Taxus wallichiana* (the Himalayan yew). Both compounds have been widely and successfully used in the treatment of a number of cancers, including those of the breast, ovary and prostate.

D-tubocurarine This alkaloid is the major poisonous component of curare (the extract of *Chondrodendron tomentosum*). It acts by blocking the action of acetylcholine on the motor end plates of the muscle, causing profound paralysis and death. However, after pure d-tubocurarine was isolated in the 1930s it was used successfully in a number of clinical situations, for example to prevent bone fractures during electroconvulsive therapy (ECT), to relax the abdominal muscles in surgery and to stop muscular spasms in strychnine poisoning.

Element (chemical) An element is a basic building block of chemistry. For example, sodium chloride (common salt) contains the metallic element sodium and the gaseous element chlorine in combination.

Emetine (Ipecacuanha) is the active alkaloid derived from the South American vomiting root (*Carapichea ipecacuanha*). Originally used by Thomas Dover in his powdered root to cause vomiting and to treat fevers, it became known as 'the poor man's quinine'. The pure alkaloid was the first available cure for the tropical disease amoebic dysentery caused by the protozoal parasite *Entamoeba histolytica*.

Enzyme An enzyme is a biological catalyst which accelerates chemical reactions in the body without itself being consumed in the process. Examples include cholinesterase, present at nerve endings, which breaks down acetylcholine; and diastase, present in saliva, which breaks down starchy foods. There are thousands of such enzymes present in the human organism. The first to be discovered was that in brewer's yeast (such as the alcohol dehydrogenase), which accelerates the breakdown of sugars to alcohol (ethyl alcohol). Conventionally all biological enzymes are given the suffix -ase; for example esterases destroy esters.

Ephedra and Ephedrine Ma Huang is an ancient Chinese drug which was used to treat coughs and respiratory diseases such a as asthma. The pure alkaloid it contains is called ephedrine and was the first oral treatment for asthma. It is a powerful adrenergic, mimicking the natural release of adrenaline (epinephrine) in the body. This effect serves to dilate the bronchi (small breathing tubes) in the lungs.

Ergot, Ergometrine and Ergotamine Ergot is a crude extract of the ergot fungus (*Claviceps purpurea*) which is a parasite of grasses (particularly rye). The impure fungal extract contains many chemical compounds such as histamine, acetylcholine, lysergic acid, diethylamide and the ergot alkaloids. Ergometrine is a pure alkaloid of ergot. It causes active contraction of the uterine muscle and is therefore used to stem post-partum bleeding together with oxytocin. Ergotamine is another pure alkaloid isolated from the crude extract of ergot. It can block the action of adrenaline on vascular muscle receptors but has much less effect on the uterine muscle. It was the first effective oral drug for migraine but causes serious problems in overdose.

Galantamine is an alkaloid found in the snowdrop (*Galanthus nivalis*) and is an anticholinesterase. It is thought that Odysseus used this plant to protect himself from Circe who had poisoned his sailors with a Solanaceous alkaloid, perhaps atropine or hyoscine. This drug has been used to treat some of the symptoms of Alzheimer's disease.

Hyoscine is an alkaloid found in henbane (*Hyoscyamus niger*), a member of the Solanaceae family. Most of its actions are similar to those of *Atropa belladonna* with the exception that it is sedative rather than excitant. It is an anticholinergic drug.

Hypericin This active compound occurs naturally in St John's wort (*Hypericum perforatum*). It has a beneficial effect in mild to moderate depression. Unfortunately its use as an over-the-counter medicine for depression has been blighted by the fact that it interacts with many prescription drugs. The concentration of these drugs in the blood can then be raised, as their metabolism in the liver is reduced, resulting on occasion in serious toxic reactions.

Lysergic acid diethylamide (LSD) is a compound found in all preparations of ergot. It has powerful effects on the mind, producing visual hallucinations and out-of-body sensations. It was once tried as a treatment for schizophrenia but if anything can make the condition worse. It is now an illegal substance under the Dangerous Drugs Act.

Mandragorine (from the mandrake) is now called Cuscohygrine. This latter also occurs in *Erythroxylon coca* (the coca plant from the Andes).

Mixture (chemical) A chemical mixture contains two or more compounds which do not react with each other. For example a simple mixture would be salt (sodium chloride) and sugar (sucrose). A complex mixture would be similar to that of curare, *Chondodendron tomentosum* and other lianas, crushed venomous ants and snake poisons, containing perhaps 30 to 40 active compounds in total.

Opium is the dried latex (rubbery exudate) of the opium poppy (*Papaver somniferum*). It is a major source of the opium alkaloids morphine, codeine and papaverine. Morphine is a powerful analgesic but in overdose can produce hallucinations and respiratory depression, and can be fatal. It, and its near congener heroin, are powerful addictive drugs. The poppy is mentioned here because it was a component of the medieval soporific sponge which also contained hyoscine and mandrake.

Paclitaxel see **Docetaxel**

Pharmacognosy is the general study of drugs of plant origin including, for example, the alkaloids, the cardiac glycosides, the terpenes and the saponins.

Pharmacology is the study of drugs and their actions on physiological and biochemical systems. These drugs can be of different origins, such as animal (for example adrenaline), plant (for example atropine) or mineral (for example magnesium sulphate). They can act on specific receptors in nervous, cardiac or muscular tissue to produce a pharmacological reaction, for example in accelerating or slowing the heart, constricting or dilating the pupil, or constricting or paralysing the muscles.

Physostigmine is one of the classic alkaloids found in the Calabar bean (*Physostigma venenosum*). It exerts its action by inhibiting cholinesterase. This can result in an accumulation of toxic levels of acetylcholine in the body, which causes cardiac arrest and muscular paralysis. It was used by the Efik chiefs in the ceremony of 'trial by ordeal'. It was also the first effective treatment developed for the muscle paralysing disease myasthenia gravis.

Quinine This alkaloid was the first effective compound found to treat malaria. It occurs in the bark of two Peruvian plants, *Cinchona officinalis* and *Cinchona ledgeriana*. The bark was known variously as Peruvian bark, Jesuit's bark or Cardinal's bark as its export to Europe was facilitated by the Roman Church. The alkaloid kills the malarial parasites (*Plasmodium* species) and is still widely used today, usually in combination with other anti-malarials such as artemesinin. Cinchona bark also contains many other alkaloids such as quinidine, cinchonine and cinchonidine. All these compounds have a very bitter taste (in common with quinine). They have little anti-plasmodial activity. Quinine is still widely used in the drinks industry as a bittering agent, for example in tonic water.

Reaction (chemical and pharmacological)
A chemical reaction is where one element (or compound) reacts with another to produce one or more different compounds. For example, sodium (an element) reacts with chlorine gas (another element) to form the compound sodium chloride.

Solanine is a tropane alkaloid found in the potato (*Solanum tuberosum*) and can cause poisoning characterised by vomiting, diarrhoea, confusion and dilated pupils. It is rarely fatal, but the patient may require the administration of intravenous fluids. The concentration of the alkaloid rises when the potato starts to go green and the eyes become prominent.

Strychnos and Strychnine Strychnine is an active alkaloid obtained from the plant *Strychnos nux vomica*. Strychnos was once referred to as the king of poisons and was widely used as an arrow poison in South America and in the medieval courts of Europe, particularly France. Strychnine is a particularly violent and effective poison, causing fits, violent muscle spasms and paralysis of the respiratory muscles; it can be fatal. This alkaloid was once used as a tonic for asthenia (weakness) and for lactating mothers. A number of accidental deaths occurred and the alkaloid was banned in the 1960s.

Synaptic gap This is the gap between the nerve cell (neurone) and it effector organ, such as a muscle cell or a secretory gland. The neurotransmitter, for example acetylcholine or adrenaline, jumps the gap and binds to receptors on the organ, to be activated. When the gap is between a nerve cell and a muscle cell it is also known as a neuromuscular junction. An example of the importance of this gap or junction is that d-tubocurarine exerts its paralytic effect by blocking the effect of acetylcholine at this strategic position.

Synthesis (chemical) This denotes the process whereby complex molecules are built up from the basic elements carbon, hydrogen, nitrogen and oxygen. As a result of the complicated structure of the alkaloids this process can take many years to complete. In particular, quinine and strychnine resisted successful synthesis until the 1940s (the alkaloids having been isolated in pure form in the 1820s).

Taxines A and B These two compounds are the principal poisonous alkaloids of the European yew (*Taxus baccata*). Taxine A is the more abundant of the two and is directly toxic to the heart, providing a fatal abnormality of rhythm. Also present in the yew are the taxels which have been developed into very effective anti-cancer agents, such as docetaxel and paclitaxel.

Thujone is a monoterpene occurring in *Artemesia absinthium* (bitter wormwood) and was added to absinthe to give it its bitter taste. It has, however, been banned as it causes unacceptable side-effects, including hallucinations and fits. It also exists at lower concentrations in the cedars and the tansy, a widely used herb.

Endnotes

Chapter 3

[1] See a modern translation in GREAVE, M.A. (ed.). *Gerard's Herbal* 1597. London: Jonathan Cape, 1931.

[2] DAURIOL, M. Nouveau procédé pour plonger dans la stupeur les maladies qui doivent subir une opération. *Journal de Médecine et Chirurgie de Toulouse*, **10** (1847): 178. An extract of the paper, entitled 'A substitute for the vapour of ether to   annul sensation during operations', was published   in the *Lancet*, i (1847): 540.

Chapter 4

[1] Luke, 8: 26–33.

Chapter 5

[1] TICKELL, T. Kensington Gardens, 1722.

[2] Homer, *The Odyssey*, Book X, translated by Samuel Butler.

[3] Ibid.

[4] PLAITAKIS, A. & DUVOISIN, R.C. Homer's moly identified as *Galanthus nivalis L*: physiologic antidote to *Stramonium* poisoning. *Clinical Neuropharmacology*, 6 (1983): 1–5.

Chapter 6

[1] SHAKESPEARE, W. *Romeo and Juliet*, Act IV Scene 4: 45–47.

[2] Genesis, 30: 14–19.

[3] THOMPSON, C.J.S. *The Mystic Mandrake*. London: Rider and Co, 1934.

[4] Ibid.

Chapter 8

[1] READER, J. *The Propitious Esculent: The Potato in World History*. London: William Heinemann, 2008.

Chapter 10

[1] WITHERING, W. *An Account of the Foxglove and some of its Medical uses; with Practical Remarks on the Dropsy, and Some Other Diseases*. London: G.G.J. and J. Robinson, 1785

[2] WITHERING, W. *A Botanical Arrangement of all the Vegetables Growing Naturally in Great Britain*. London: Cadel and Elmsley, 1776.

Chapter 11

[1] BRUNETON, J. *Pharmacognosy, Phytochemistry of Medicinal Plants*. Andover: Intercept, 1995.

[2] STRONG, L.A.G. *Doctor Quicksilver 1660–1742. The Life and Times of Thomas Dover MD*. London: Andrew Melrose, 1955.

Chapter 12

[1] Jeremiah, 23: 15.

Chapter 14

[1] Quoted in BOULGER, G.S. *Familiar Trees*. London: Cassel and Co., n.d.

Chapter 15

[1] COPEMAN, W.S.C. *A Short History of the Gout and the Rheumatic Diseases*. Berkeley and Los Angeles: University of California Press, 1964.

[2] Ibid.

Chapter 16

[1] LONITZER, A. *Kräuterbuch*. Frankfurt am Main: Christian Egenolff, 1582.

[2] BARGER, G. *Ergot and Ergotism*. London: Gurney and Jackson, 1931.

[3] DARWIN, E. *The Botanic Garden*. London: J. Johnson, 1791.

[4] THOMS, H. John Stearns and *pulvis parturiens*. *American Journal of Obstetrics and Gynecology*, 22 (1931): 418–423.

[5] HOFMANN, A. LSD: *My Problem Child*. New York: McGraw Hill, 1980.

Sources

Chapter 1

CULPEPER, N. *Complete Herball* n.p., 1653. Modern edition published as *Culpeper's Complete Herbal and English Physician*. London: P.W. Foulsham & Co. Ltd, 1960.

DUNCAN, A. *The Edinburgh New Dispensary*. Edinburgh: n.p., 1803.

HYAM, R. & PANKHURST, R. *Plants and their Names: A Concise Dictionary*. Oxford: Oxford University Press, 1995.

LEE, M.R. The snowdrop (*Galanthus nivalis*): from Odysseus to Alzheimer. *Proceedings of the Royal College of Physicians of Edinburgh*, 29 (1999): 349–352.

LEE, M.R. The mandrake. *Journal of the Royal College of Physicians of Edinburgh*, 36 (2006): 278–285.

MATTIOLI, P.A. *Di Pedacio Dioscoride Anazarbeo Libri cinque Della historia, et materia medicinale tradotti in lingua volgare italiana da M. Pietro Andrea Matthiolo Sanese Medico, con amplissimi discorsi, et comenti, et dottissime annotationi, et censure del medesimo interprete*, also known as *Discorsi*, n.p., 1544.

PICKERING, D. *Dictionary of Witchcraft*. London: Cassell Publishers, 1996.

POLSON, C.J., GREEN, M.A. & LEE, M.R. *Clinical Toxicology*, 3rd edition. London: Pitman Books Ltd, 1983.

The Scotsman, 20 January to 21 February 1995.

SNEADER, W. *Drug Discovery: The Evolution of Modern Medicines*. Chichester: John Wiley and Sons, 1985.

WITTHAUS, R.A. *Manual of Toxicology*, 2nd edition. New York: Baillière, Tindall and Cox, 1911.

Chapter 2

BALFOUR, J.H. Description of the plant which produces the Ordeal Bean of Calabar. *Transactions of the Royal Society of Edinburgh*, 22 (1860): 305–312.

CHRISTISON, R. On the properties of the ordeal bean of Old Calabar. *Monthly Journal of Medicine*, 20 (1855): 193–204.

CRUM BROWN, A. & FRASER, T.R. On the connection between chemical constitution and physiological action. *Transactions of the Royal Society*, XXV (1868): 8.

DALE, H.H., FELDBERG, W. & VOGT, M. Release of acetylcholine at voluntary muscle nerve endings. *Journal of Physiology*, 86 (1936): 353–380.

DRAGSTEDT, C.A. Trial by ordeal. *Quarterly Bulletin of the North Western Medical School*, 13 (1945): 137–141.

FELDBERG, W.W. Henry Hallett Dale (1875–1968): a memorial. *British Journal of Pharmacology*, 35 (1969): 1–9.

FRASER, T.R. On the characters, actions and therapeutic uses of the bean of Calabar. *Edinburgh Medical Journal*, 9 (1863): 36–56, 123–132, 235–248.

HOSKINS, R. *The Boy in the River: A Shocking True Case of Murder and Sacrifice in the Heart of London*. London: Pan Books, 2012.

JOBST, J. & HESSE, O. Ueber die Bohne von Calabar. *Annalen der Chemie und Pharmacie*, 129 (1864): 115–121.

LEE, M.R. The miracle at St Alfege's: 70 years on. *Journal of the Royal Society of Medicine*, 100 (2007): 108–109.

WALKER, M.E. Treatment of myasthenia gravis with physostigmine. *Lancet*, 226 (1934): 1200–1201.

Chapter 3

BAROJA, J.C. *The World of Witches*. London: Weidenfeld and Nicolson, 1964. Translated by Nigel Glendenning.

British National Formulary, 64th edition. British Medical Association & Royal Pharmaceutical Society, 2012.

BROWNE, D.G. & TULLETT, E.V. (eds) *Spilsbury G. His Life and Cases*. London: George G. Harrap & Co. Ltd.

CARTER, A.J. Narcosis and nightshade. *British Medical Journal*, 313 (1996): 1630–1632.

Dictionary of National Biography. Oxford: Oxford University Press, 2004.

GRAVES, R. *The Greek Myths*, London: Penguin Books, 1995, 2 vols.

GREAVE, M.A. (ed.) *Gerard's Herbal 1597*. London: Jonathan Cape, 1931.

PICKERING, D. *Cassell's Dictionary of Witchcraft*. London: Cassell, 1996.

SQUIRE, W. *Squire's Companion to the British Pharmacopoeia*, 18th edition. London: J and A Churchill, 1908.

WEIGHTMAN, G. *Signor Marconi's Magic Box*. London: Harper Collins, 2003. Chapter 36 describes the arrest of Crippen and Le Neve on the SS *Montrose*.

Chapter 4

BENTLEY, J. *A Calendar of Saints: The Lives of the Principal Saints of the Christian Year*. London: Little, Brown & Co., 1986.

BOVE, G.M. Acute neuropathy after exposure to the sun in a patient treated with St John's wort. *Lancet*, 353 (1998): 1121–1122.

BRUNETON, J. *Pharmacognosy, Phytochemistry and Medicinal Plants*. Andover: Intercept Ltd, 1995.

DARWIN, T. *The Scots Herbal. The Plant Lore of Scotland*. Edinburgh: Mercat Press, 1996.

DE SMET, P.A.G.M. & NOLEN, W.A. St John's wort as an antidepressant. *British Medical Journal*, 313 (1996): 241–242.

GERARD, J. *Herball*, London: n.p., 1597.

HYAM, R. & PANKHURST, R. *Plants and their Names: A Concise Dictionary*. Oxford: Oxford University Press, 1995.

KATZENSTEIN, L. *Secrets of St. John's Wort*. London: Hodder and Stoughton, 1998.

LAAKMANN, G., SCHULE, C., BAGHAIL, T. & KIESER, M. St. John's wort in mild to moderate depression: the relevance of hyperforin for clinical efficacy. *Pharmacopsychiatry*, 31 (1998) (Supplement 1): 54–59.

LIGHTFOOT, J. *Flora Scotia*. London: n.p., 1777.

LINDE, K., RAMIREZ, G., MULROW, C.D., PAULS, A., WEIDENHAMMER, W. & MELCHART, D. St. John's wort for depression – an overview and meta-analysis of randomised clinical trials. *British Medical Journal*, 313 (1996): 253–258.

MABEY, R. *Flora Britannica*. London: Sinclair Stevenson, 1996.

MURCH, S.J., SIMMONS, C.B. & SAXENA, P.K. Melatonin in feverfew and other medicinal plants. *Lancet*, 350 (ii) (1997): 1598–1599.

Chapter 5

AGARWAL, H.C. & GUPTA, S.E. Ocular hypotensive effect of galanthamine hydrobromide: an experimental study. *Indian Journal of Pharmacology*, 22 (1990): 117–118.

ALZHEIMER, A. Über eine eigenartigen schweren Krankheitsprozess der Hirnrinde. *Neurolisches Zentralblatt*, 25 (1906): 1134.

BEIGHTON, P. & BEIGHTON, G. *Alois Alzheimer. The Man behind the Syndrome*. Berlin and New York: Springer Verlag, 1986.

CHURCH, Rev. A.H. *The Story of the Odyssey*, 3rd edition. London: Steeley & Co., 1903.

COZANITIS, D.A. Experiences with galanthamine and its analogues. *Pharmacology & Therapeutics*, 68 (1995): 129–136.

GRAVES, R. *The Greek Myths*. Harmondsworth: Penguin Books, 1960.

HARBORNE, J., BAXTER, H. & MOSS, G. (eds) *Dictionary of Plant Toxins*. Chichester: John Wiley, 1996.

HARVEY, A.L. The pharmacology of galanthamine and its analogues. *Pharmacology & Therapeutics*, 68 (1995): 113–128.

HYAM, R. & PANKHURST, R. *Plants and their Names: A Concise Dictionary*. Oxford: Oxford University Press, 1995.

MABEY, R. *Flora Britannica*. London: Sinclair Stevenson, 1996.

MORRIS, L.C., CYRUS, P.A., ORAZEM, J., MAS, J., BIEBER, F., RUZICKA, B.B. & GULANSKI, B. Metrifonate benefits cognitive behavioral, and global function in patients with Alzheimer's disease. *Neurology*, 50 (1998): 1222–1230.

RAINER, M. Clinical studies with Galanthamine. *Drugs Today*, 33 (1997): 273–279.

THOMSEN, T., BICKEL, U., FISCHER, J.P. & KEWITZ, H. Galanthamine hydrobromide as a long term treatment of Alzheimer's disease. *Dementia*, 1 (1990): 46–51.

Chapter 6

CHEVALIER, A. *Encyclopedia of Medicinal Plants*. London: Dorling Kindersley, 1996.

GREENBLATT, R.B. *Search the Scriptures*. Carnforth: Parthenon Press, 1985.

RICHARDSON, B.W. The production and physiological action of the mandrake. *Asclepiad*, V (1888): 183–188.

SHAKESPEARE, W. *Romeo and Juliet*. London: Penguin, 2005.

STRATMANN, L. *Chloroform: The Quest for Oblivion*. Stroud: Sutton Publishing, 2003.

THOMPSON, C.J.S. *Greece*. London: Rider and Co., 1934.

Chapter 7

BENNETT, A.E. Preventing traumatic complication in convulsive shock therapy by curare. *The Journal of the American Medical Association*, 114 (1940): 322–324.

BERNARD, C. New experiments on the Woorara poison, *Lancet*, 57 (1851): 298.

BROWNE, D. & TULLETT, E.V. *Bernard Spilsbury: His Life and Cases*. Harmondsworth: Penguin Books (1955).

BUCKINGHAM, J. *Bitter Nemesis: The Intimate History of Strychnine*. Boca Raton, FL: CRC Press, 2008.

CHRISTISON, Sir R., On the properties of the Ordeal bean of Old Calabar. *Monthly Journal of Medicine*, 20 (1855): 193–204.

CILL, R.C. *White Water and Black Magic*. New York: Henry Holt and Company, Inc., 1940.

DALE, H.H., FELDBERG, H. & VOGT, M. The release of acetylcholine at voluntary muscle nerve endings. *Journal of Physiology*, 86 (1936): 353–380.

GRAY, T.C. d-Tubocurarine chloride, *Proceedings of the Royal Society of Medicine*, 41 (1948): 559–568.

GRIFFITH, H.R. & JOHNSON, G.E. The use of curare in general anesthesia, *Anesthesiology*, 3 (4) (1942): 642–644.

KING, H. Alkaloids of some *Chondrodendron* species and the origin of *Radix pareira*. *Journal of the Chemical Society*, 0 (1940): 737–738.

RUIZ, H. & PAVAN, J. *Systema Vegetabilium Florae Peruvianae et Chilensis*. Madrid: Typis Gabrielis de Sancha, 1798.

VON HUMBOLDT, A. & BONPLAND, A. *Voyages aux régions équinoxiales du nouveau continent*, Paris: n.p., 1807.

WATERTON, C. *Wanderings in South America, the North West of the United States and the Antilles*. London: J. Mauman & Co., 1825.

WINTERSTEINER, D. & DUTSCHER, J.D. Curare alkaloids from *Chondrodendron tomentosum*. *Science*, 97 (1943): 353–358.

Chapter 8

MCCONNELL, A.A. & REID, D.T. The Irish famine: a century and a half on. *Proceedings of the Royal College of Physicians Edinburgh*, 28 (1998): 383–394.

MCMILLAN, M. & THOMPSON, J.C. An outbreak of suspected solanine poisoning in school boys: examination of the criteria for solanine poisoning. *Quarterly Journal of Medicine*, 190 (1979): 227–243.

READER, J. *The Propitious Esculent: The Potato in World History*. London: William Heinemann, 2008.

ZUCKERMAN, L. *The Potato: How the Humble Spud Rescued the Western World*. Boston, MA: Faber and Faber, 1998.

Chapter 9

AMATSU, H. & KUBOTA, S. Über die pharmakologischen Wirkung des Ephedrins und Mydriatins. *Kyoto Igaka Zassi*, 10 (1913): 301–309.

ANON. Begrüßung von Professor Dr. W.N. Nagai. *Berichte der Deutschen Chemischen Gesellschaft*, 60 (1927): 167–175.

BARGER, G. & DALE, H.H. Chemical structure and sympathomimetic action of amines. *Journal of Physiology*, 41 (1910): 19–59.

BRUNETON, J. *Pharmacognosy, Phytochemistry and Medicinal Plants*. Andover: Intercept Ltd, 1995.

COOPER, P. *Poisoning by Drugs and Chemicals*, 3rd edition. London: Alchemist Publications, 1974.

DOLLERY, C. (ed.) *Therapeutic Drugs*, vol. I. Edinburgh: Churchill Livingstone, 1991.

HUANG, K.C. *The Pharmacology of Chinese Herbs*, 2nd edition. Boca Raton, FL: CRC Press, 1999.

HYAM, R. & PANKHURST, R. *Plants and their Names: A Concise Dictionary*. Oxford: Oxford University Press, 1995.

MILLER, T.G. Ephedrine: its use in the treatment of vascular hypotension and bronchial asthma. *Annals of Clinical Medicine*, 4 (1926): 713–721.

MIURA, K. Vorläufige Mitteilung über Ephedrin, ein neues Mydriaticum. *Berliner Klinische Wochenschrift*, 24 (1887): 907–911.

RASMUSSEN, N. *On Speed: The Many Lives of Amphetamine*. New York: New York University Press, 2008.

SCHEINDLIN, S. Ephedra: once a boon, now a bane. *Molecular Interventions*, 3 (2003): 358–360.

Chapter 10

ARONSON, J.K. *An Account of the Foxglove and its Medical Uses 1785–1985*. Oxford: Oxford University Press, 1985.

MOORMAN, L.J. William Withering and his work, his health, his friends. *Bulletin of the History of Medicine*, 12 (1942): 355–366.

WITHERING, W. Experiments upon the different kinds of marle found in Staffordshire. *Philosophical Transactions*, lxiii (1773): 161–166.

WITHERING, W. *A Botanical Arrangement of all the Vegetables Naturally Growing in Great Britain*. London: Cadell, Elmsley and Robinson, 1776.

WITHERING, W. An account of a convenient method of inhaling the vapour of volatile substances. *Annals of Medicine*, iii (1799): 447–451.

WITHERING, W. Experiments and observations on the *Terra Ponderosa*. *Philosophical Transactions*, lxxiv (1784): 293–311.

WITHERING, W. *An Account of the Foxglove and some of its Medical Uses; with Practical Remarks on the Dropsy, and some other Diseases*. London: G.G.J. and J. Robinson, 1785.

Chapter 11

BRUNETON, J. *Pharmacognosy, Phytochemistry and Medicinal Plants*. Andover: Intercept Ltd, 1995.

COX, F.E.G. (ed.) *The Wellcome Trust Illustrated History of Tropical Diseases*. London: Wellcome Trust, 1996.

CUMMING, I. *Helvetius: His Life and Place in the History of Educational Thought.* London: Routledge & Kegan Paul, 1955.

DIAMOND, L.S. Axenic cultivation of *Entamoeba histolytica. Science*, 134 (1961): 336–337.

DOLLERY, C. (ed.) *Therapeutic Drugs*, vol. I. Edinburgh: Churchill Livingstone, 1991.

LEE, M.R. Plants against malaria. Part 1: Cinchona or the Peruvian bark. *Journal of the Royal College of Physicians Edinburgh*, 32 (2002): 189–196.

LEE, M.R. Curare. The South American arrow poison. *Journal of the Royal College of Physicians Edinburgh*, 35 (2005): 83–92.

LÖSCH, F.A. Massive development of amoebae in the large intestine (in translation). *American Journal of Tropical Medicine and Hygiene*, 24 (1975): 383–392.

PELLETIER, J. & MAGENDIE, F. Recherches chimiques et physiologiques sur l'ipecacuanha. *Annales de Chimie et Physique*, 4 (1817): 172–185.

ROGERS, L. The rapid cure of amoebic dysentery and hepatitis by hypodermic injection of soluble salts of emetine. *British Medical Journal*, i (1912): 1424–1425.

STRONG, L.A.G. *Doctor Quicksilver 1660–1742. The Life and Times of Thomas Dover MD.* London: Andrew Melrose, 1955.

WILMOT, A.J., POWELL, S.J. & ADAMS, E.B. The comparative value of emetine and chloroquine in amebic liver abscess. *American Journal of Tropical Medicine and Hygiene*, 7 (1958): 197–198.

Chapter 12

HUANG, K.C. *The Pharmacology of Chinese Herbs*, 2nd edition. Boca Raton, FL: CRC Press, 1999.

HYAM, R. & PANKHURST, R. *Plants and their Names: A Concise Dictionary.* Oxford: Oxford University Press, 1995..

KASTER, J. *The Concise Mythological Dictionary.* London: Peerage Books, 1989.

LI, G.Q., GUO, X.B., JIN, R., WANG, Z.C., JIAN, H.X. & LI, Z.Y. Clinical studies on the treatment of cerebral malaria with qinghaosu and its derivatives. *Journal of Traditional Medicine*, 2 (1982): 125–130.

MANN, J. *Murder, Magic and Medicine.* Oxford: Oxford University Press, 1992.

QINGHAOSU ANTIMALARIA COORDINATING RESEARCH GROUP. Antimalaria studies on qinghaosu. *Chinese Medical Journal*, 12 (1979): 811–816.

SHWE, T., MYINT, P.T., MYINT, W., HTUT, Y., SOE, L. & THWE, M. Clinical studies on treatment of cerebral malaria with artemether and mefloquine. *Transactions of the Royal Society of Tropical Medicine and Hygiene*, 83 (1989): 489–490.

SPILLIUS, A. The cure the West ignored. *Daily Telegraph Magazine*, 1 September 2001: 50–55.

WHITE, N.J. Qinghaosu combinations. *Médecine Tropicale*, 58 (1998): 85–88.

Chapter 13

BRUCE-CHWATT, L.J. Oliver Cromwell's medical history. *Transactions of the College of Physicians of Philadelphia*, 4 (1984): 98–121.

BRUNETON, J. *Pharmacognosy, Phytochemistry and Medicinal Plants.* Andover: Intercept Ltd, 1995

DE LA CONDAMINE, C. *Sur l'arbre du Quinquina.* Paris: Académie Royale des Sciences, 1738.

DOBSON, M.J. Bitter-sweet solutions for malaria: exploring natural remedies from the past. *Parassitologia*, 40 (1998): 69–81.

DOLLERY, C. (ed.) *Therapeutic Drugs*, vol. II. Edinburgh: Churchill Livingstone, 1991.

GRAMICCIA, G. *The Life of Charles Ledger (1818–1905). Alpacas and Quinine.* Basingstoke and London: Macmillan Press (1988).

JARCHO, S. *Quinine's Predecessor. Francesco Torti and the Early History of Cinchona.* Baltimore, MD and London: Johns Hopkins University Press, 1993.

LAVERAN, A. Note sur un nouveau parasite trouvé dans le sang de plusieurs malades atteints de fièvre palustre. *Bulletin de l'Académie de Médecine de Paris*, 9 (1880): 1235–1236, 1346–1347.

MARKHAM, C. *Peruvian Bark.* London: John Murray, 1880.

MCMAINS, H.F. *The Death of Oliver Cromwell.* Lexington, KY: University Press of Kentucky, 2000.

PELLETIER, P. & CAVENTOU, J. Recherches chimiques sur les quinquinas. *Annales de Chimie et Physique* 15 (1820): 337–367.

POSER, C.M. & BRUYN, G.W. *An Illustrated History of Malaria.* New York and London: Parthenon Press, 1999.

TALBOR, R. *The English Remedy: or Talbor's Wonderful Secret for curing Agues and Fevers.* London: J. Hindmarsh, 1682.

TORTI, F. *Therapeutice Specialis ad Febres Quaedam Perniciosas.* Modena: B Soliani, 1712.

WEDDELL, H. *Histoire naturelle des quinquinas.* Paris: Victor Masson, 1849.

WOODWARD, R. and DOERING, W. 'Synthesis of quinine. *Journal of the American Chemistry Society*, 66 (1944): 849 and 67 (1945): 860.

Chapter 14

BOULGER, G.S. *Familiar Trees.* London: Cassell and Co., n.d.

COOPER, P. *Poisoning*, 3rd edition. London: Alchemist Publications, 1974.

Daily Mail, 25 November 2008.

GREGORY, R.E. & DELISA, A.F. Paclitaxel; a new anti-neoplastic agent for refractory ovarian cancer. *Clinical Pharmacology*, 12 (1993): 401–415.

HURT, S. Poisonous effects of the berries, or seeds, of the yew. *Lancet*, 693 (1836): 394–395.

Irish Independent, 12 April 2008.

NICOLAU, K.C., DAI, W.M. & GUY, R.K. Chemistry and biology of Taxol. *Angewandte Chemie*, 33 (1994): 15–44.

SHAKESPEARE, W. *Macbeth.* London: Penguin, 2005.

SHAKESPEARE, W. *Twelfth Night.* London: Penguin, 2005.

VAN DER WERTH, J. & MURPHY, J.J. Cardiovascular toxicity associated with yew leaf ingestion. *British Heart Journal*, 72 (1994): 92–93.

WANI, M.C., TAYLOR, H.L., WALL, M.E., COGGON, P. & MCPHAIL, M.T. Plant antitumor agents. VI. The isolation and structure of taxol, a novel antileukemic and antitumor agent from *Taxus brevifolia. Journal of the American Chemistry Society*, 93 (1971): 2325–2327.

WILKS, J.S. *Trees of the British Isles in History and Legend.* London: Frederick Muller, 1972.

Chapter 15

COOPER, P. *Poisoning by Drugs and Chemicals.* London: Alchemist Publications, 1958.

COPEMAN, W.S.C. *A Short History of the Gout and the Rheumatic Diseases.* Berkeley, CA: University of California Press (1964).

DOLLERY, C. (ed.) *Therapeutic Drugs*, vol. I & vol. II. Edinburgh: Churchill Livingstone, 1991.

FLESCH, F., KINTZ, P., KRENCKER, E., IHADADENE, N., SAUDER, P. & JAEGER, A. Food mistake: a case of poisoning by ingesting autumn crocus, *European Journal of Emergency Medicine*, 8 (1) (2001): 73–74.

GODDEN JONES, E. *An Account of the Remarkable Effects of the Eau Médicinale d'Husson in the Gout.* London: John Murray, 1810.

HOUDÉ, A. De la colchicine cristallisée. *Comptes Rendus Hebdomadaires des Sciences et Mémoires de la Société de Biologie*, 1 (8) (1884): 218–220.

LEE, M.R. The yew in mythology and medicine. *Proceedings of the Royal College of Physicians Edinburgh*, 28 (1998): 569–575.

MATZNER, Y. Biologic and clinical advances in Familial Mediterranean Fever. *Critical Reviews in Oncology/Hematology*, 18 (1995): 197–205.

PELLÉTIER, P. & CAVENTOU, J. Examen clinique de plusieurs végétaux de la famille des colchicées et du principe actif qu'ils renferment. *Annales de Chimie et de Physique*, 14 (1820): 69–83.

SCHEELE, K.W. *Chemical Essays.* Translated by T. Beddoes. London: John Murray, 1786.

WILSON, J.D., BRAUNWALD, E., ISSELBACHER, K.J., PETERSDORF, R.G., MARTIN, J.B., FAUCI, A.S. & ROOT, R.K. (eds) *Harrison's Principles of Internal Medicine*, 12th edition. New York: McGraw-Hill Inc., 1991.

Chapter 16

See www.erowid.org/references/refs.php for a complete list of LSD research papers.

BARGER, G. *Ergot and Ergotism.* London: Gurney and Jackson, 1931.

COHEN, S. A classification of LSD complications. *Psychosomatics*, 7 (1966): 182–186.

Daily Telegraph, 20 May 2008 (Obituary of Albert Hofmann).

DARWIN, E. *The Botanic Garden.* London: J. Johnson, 1791.

GEOFFROY, C.J. Observations sur la structure et l'usage des principales parties des fleurs. *Mémoire de l'Académie Royale des Sciences* (1711): 207–230.

HOFMANN, A. *LSD: My Problem Child.* New York: McGraw-Hill Inc., 1980.

LONITZER, A. *Kräuterbuch.* Frankfurt am Main: Christian Egenolff, 1582.

PRESCOTT, O. *A Dissertation on the Natural History and Medicinal Effects of the Secale cornutum or Ergot.* Boston, MA: Cummings and Hilliard, 1813.

SMART, R.G. & BATEMAN, K. Unfavourable reactions to LSD: a review and analysis of the available case reports. *Canadian Medical Association Journal*, 97 (1967): 1214–1221.

STEARNS, J. Account of the *pulvis parturiens*, a remedy for quickening childbirth. *Medical Repository of New York*, 5 (1808): 308–309.

STOLL, A. & HOFMANN, A. Partialsynthese von Alkaloiden vom Typus des Ergobasins. *Helvetica Chimica Acta*, 26 (1943): 944–965.

STOLL, W.A. Lysergsäure-diäthyl-amid, ein Phantastikum aus der Mutterkorngruppe. *Schweizer Archiv für Neurologie und Psychiatrie*, 60 (1947): 279.

THOMS, H. John Stearns and *pulvis parturiens*. *American Journal of Obstetrics and Gynecology*, 22 (1931): 418–423.

TULASNE, L.R. Mémoire sur l'ergot des glumacées. *Annales de Science Naturelle Botanique*, 3 (1853): 5–56.

VON MÜNCHHAUSEN, O. *Der Hausvater. Part I.* Hannover: N Försters und Sohns Erben, 1764.

Acknowledgements

This volume is based on a series of articles on plant poisons published in the *Journal of the Royal College of Physicians of Edinburgh* over the period 1997–2009. The material has now been adapted for the general reader. I am grateful to the President and Fellows of the Edinburgh College, who have vested the copyright in me and enabled the present volume to be published by the Royal Botanic Garden Edinburgh. I am also grateful to the following individuals and institutions:

First, to the Regius Keeper of the Garden, Simon Milne and to Doctor A.D. Toft, former President of the Royal College of Physicians in Edinburgh, for their support and generous forewords.

Second, to the following libraries for their assistance:

In Edinburgh:
The National Library of Scotland
The Royal Botanic Garden Edinburgh
The Royal College of Physicians of Edinburgh
The Royal Society

In London:
The Linnaean Society
The Royal College of Obstetrics and Gynaecology
The Royal College of Physicians (Munk's Roll)
The Royal Pharmaceutical Society
The Royal Society
The Royal Society of Chemstry

Third, I am particularly grateful to the following individuals who have played a significant role at various times in the prolonged gestation of this volume.

Hamish Adamson, Caroline Muir and Alice Young of the Publications department at RBGE.

Anna Stevenson and Greg Kenicer.

May Gibb, my secretary for a number of years.

Jane Hutcheon, formerly Head of the Library at RBGE.

Anne Lennon, who reviewed the manuscript.

Iain Milne and Estela Dukan of the Sibbald Library RCPE.

My physicians and surgeons, Hilary Devlin, Andrew Flapan, William Uttley and Caroline Whitworth, without whose help I would not have survived to tell this tale.

Finally I would like to thank my wife Judith, my best beloved, for all of her patience and tolerance during a difficult time.

Credits

The publishers would like to thank the following for permission to reproduce images in this publication. Every effort has been made to trace holders of copyright. Should there be any inadvertent omissions or errors the publishers will be pleased to correct them for future editions.

Top (t) Bottom (b) Right (r) Left (l) Middle (m)

pp 11, 12, 14, 16, 22(l), 22(r), 23 (t), 24, 25 (l), 25 (r), 25 (b), 26, 36, 37, 40, 42 (t), 46, 47, 48 (t), 48 (b), 53, 54, 55, 56, 57, 58, 61, 62 (t), 62 (b), 64, 65 (b), 70, 78 (r), 78 (l), 79, 85, 87 (t), 87 (b), 88, 93, 97 (l), 97 (m), 97 (r), 99, 100, 101 (b), 102 (b), 105, 107, 108 (t), 108 (b), 109, 110 (t), 110 (b), 111, 112 (t) 112 (b), 117, 120, 124 (t), 124 (b), 125, 127, 128 (t), 128 (b), 129, 133, 134 Wellcome Library, London

pp 13, 45, 67, 86, 104, 118 Mary Evans Picture Library

pp 17, 23 (b), 29, 49, 50, 65 (t), 69, 71, 72, 73, 82, 90, 101 (t), 102 (t), 132 Science Photo Library

p. 27 © Alasdair Young

p. 30 Reproduction by Courtesy of the British Dental Association

p. 31 Portrait of Catherine Monvoisin (La Voisin) (1640-80) (engraving) (b/w photo), French School, (17th century)/Bibliotheque Nationale, Paris, France/ Bridgeman Images

p. 32 © Crown Copyright: RCAHMS. Licensor www.rcahms.gov.uk

p. 34 Mrs Cora Crippen (b/w photo), English Photographer, (19th century)/Private Collection/ Bridgeman Images

p.35 (t) The arrest of Dr Crippen, July 1910 (b/w photo), English Photographer, (20th century)/Private Collection/© Look and Learn/Elgar Collection/Bridgeman Images, (b) The London Murder Mystery (engraving), English School, (19th century)/Private Collection/© Look and Learn/Peter Jackson Collection/Bridgeman Images

p. 42 (b) © Lukrecije | Dreamstime.com - Herbal Oil Made Of St John's Wort Photo

p. 74 (t) Portrait of Antoine Parmentier (1737-1813) 1812 (oil on canvas), Dumont, Francois (1751-1831)/Château de Versailles, France/Bridgeman

p. 81 (t) © Royal College of Physicians London

p. 81 (b) Royal Pharmaceutical Society Museum

p. 83 © Joseph Sohm/Visions of America/Corbis

p. 89 By permission of the Linnean Society of London, www.linnean.org

p. 95 By permission of John Bell & Croyden www.johnbellcroyden.co.uk

p. 116 © Crown Copyright: Courtesy of the Forestry Commission

p. 136 © STR/Keystone/Corbis

The following are the sources for the plant images, taken from the Library Collection of the Royal Botanic Garden Edinburgh.

p. 10 *Atropa Belladonna* L., p. 20 *Physostigma venenosum* Balfour, p. 84 *Digitalis purpurea* L., p. 92. *Cephaelis Ipecacuanha* Willd., p. 107 *Cinchona officinalis* Hook. fil., p. 122 *Colchicum autumnale* L., p. 130 *Claviceps purpurea* Tul. from Pabst, G. (ed) Köhler's Medizinal-Pflanzen in naturgetreuen Abbildungen mit kurz erläuterndem Texte. Band 3 (Ergänzungs), Verlag von Fr. Eugen Köhler. (1883-1887)] [Artist: Walther Müller]

p. 28 *Hyoscyamus niger* L., p. 98 *Artemisia absinthium* L. Pabst, G. (ed) Köhler's Medizinal Pflanzen in naturgretenen Abbildungen mit kurz erläuterndem Texte. Band 1. Gera-Untermhaus: Verlag von Fr. Eugen Köhler. (1883-1887)] [Artist: Walther Müller]

p. 38 *Hypericum perforatum* L., p. 44 *Galanthus nivalis* L., p. 144 *Taxus baccata* L. from Thome, O.W., Flora von Deutschland, Osterreich und der Schweiz in Wort und Bild fur Schule und Haus., Friedrich von Zezschwitz, 1907.

p. 52 *Mandragora officinarum* L. original artwork by Bessie Darling Inglis (1902-1999), produced for unpublished book on 'Plants of the Bible.' Text to have been written by Harold Roy Fletcher (1907-1978), Regius Keeper, RBGE, 1956-1971.

p. 61 *Chondrodendron tomentosum* Ruiz & Pav. from Bentley, R. & Trimen, H. Medicinal Plants, being desriptions with original figures of the principal plants employed in medicine. Volume 1. Ranunculaceae to Anacardiaceae. London: J. & A. Churchill. (1875) Plate 11. Artist: David Blair

p. 63 *Strychnos nux vomica* from Pabst, G. (ed) Köhler's Medizinal Pflanzen in naturgretenen Abbildungen mit kurz erläuterndem Texte. Band 2. Gera-Untermhaus: Verlag von Fr. Eugen Köhler. (1888-1890)] [Artist: Walther Müller]

p. 68 *Solanum tuberosum* L. from Plenck, J.J. Icones plantarum medicinalium secundum systema. Vol. 2. Tab. 121 (1789)]

p. 76 *Ephedra sinica*

The publisher wishes to thank Amy Fokinther, Graham Hardy and Lynsey Wilson for their help with the images, and Elspeth Haston, Greg Kenicer and Colin Pendry for their help with the text.

Index

Note: Page numbers in *italic* indicate illustrations, those in **bold** indicate Glossary entries.